It's another great book from CGP...

OK, so GCSE Maths can be seriously challenging — and the latest courses are tougher than ever. To do well, you'll need plenty of practice at answering the type of questions you'll face in the final exams.

And you guessed it... this brilliant CGP book is brimming with realistic exam-style questions, all up-to-date for the new GCSE requirements!

We've also included fully-worked answers, so if you drop any marks, it's easy to find out exactly where you went wrong.

CGP — still the best! ☺

Our sole aim here at CGP is to produce the highest quality books — carefully written, immaculately presented and dangerously close to being funny.

Then we work our socks off to get them out to you — at the cheapest possible prices.

Contents

☑ Use the tick boxes to check off the topics you've completed.

Section Five — Geometry and Measures

Section Six — Pythagoras and Trigonometry

Section Seven — Probability and Statistics

Practice Papers

How to get answers for the Practice Papers
Worked solutions to all three practice papers are available online for you to download or print.
Go to **www.cgpbooks.co.uk/gcsemathsanswers** to get hold of them.

Published by CGP

Editors:
Rob Harrison, Shaun Harrogate, Alison Palin, David Ryan, Caley Simpson, Ruth Wilbourne.

Contributors:
Alastair Duncombe.

With thanks to Jane Appleton, Simon Little and Sarah Oxley for the proofreading.

Clipart from Corel®
Printed by Elanders Ltd, Newcastle upon Tyne

Based on the classic CGP style created by Richard Parsons.

How to Use This Book

- Hold the book <u>upright</u>, approximately <u>50 cm</u> from your face, ensuring that the text looks like <u>this</u>, not ⁵¹ᵁᵀ. Alternatively, place the book on a <u>horizontal</u> surface (e.g. a table or desk) and sit adjacent to the book, at a distance which doesn't make the text too small to read.

- In case of emergency, press the two halves of the book together <u>firmly</u> in order to close.

- Before attempting to use this book, familiarise yourself with the following <u>safety information</u>:

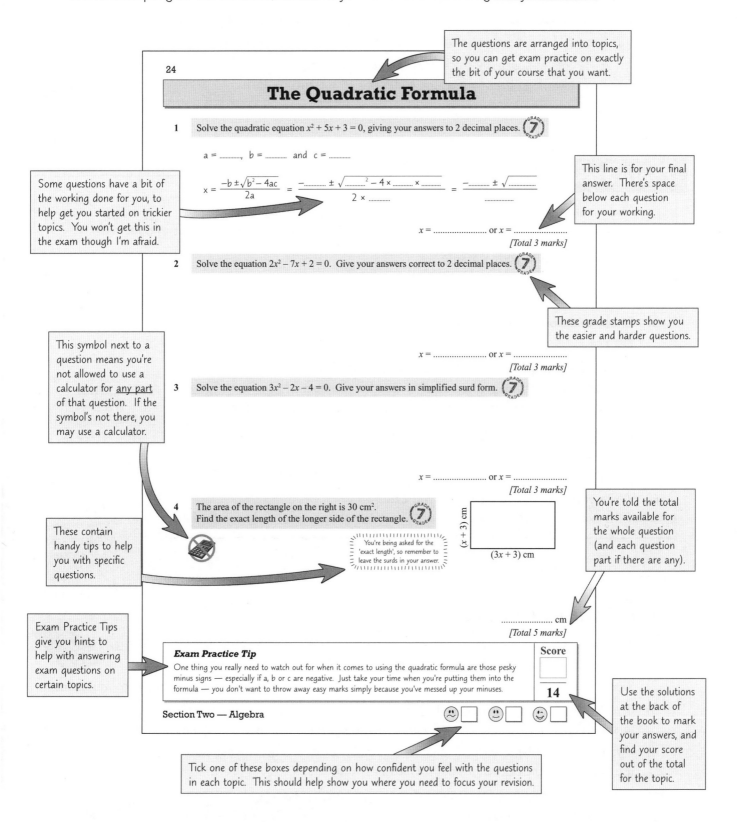

Exam Tips

Exam Stuff

Timings in the exam are really important, so here's a quick guide...

- Aim to spend about a <u>minute per mark</u> working on each question (i.e. 2 marks = 2 mins). Don't spend ages and ages on a question that's only worth a few marks.

- If you have any time left at the end of the exam, use it to <u>check</u> back through your answers and make sure you haven't made any silly mistakes. <u>Not</u> to just stare at the hottie in front.

- If you're totally, hopelessly stuck on a question, just <u>leave it</u> and <u>move on</u> to the next one. You can always <u>go back</u> to it at the end if you've got enough time.

There are a Few Golden Rules

1) **Always, always, always make sure you <u>read the question properly</u>.**
   For example, if the question asks you to give your answer in metres, <u>don't</u> give it in centimetres.

2) **Show <u>each step</u> in your <u>working</u>.**
   You're less likely to make a mistake if you write things out in stages. And even if your final answer's wrong, you'll probably pick up <u>some marks</u> if the examiner can see that your <u>method</u> is right.

3) **Check that your answer is <u>sensible</u>.**
   Worked out an angle of 450° or 0.045° in a triangle? You've probably gone wrong somewhere...

4) **Make sure you give your answer to the right <u>degree of accuracy</u>.**
   The question might ask you to round to a certain number of <u>significant figures</u> or <u>decimal places</u>. So make sure you do just that, otherwise you'll almost certainly lose marks.

5) **Look at the number of <u>marks</u> a question is worth.**
   If a question's worth 2 or more marks, you probably won't get them all for just writing down the final answer — you're going to have to <u>show your working</u>.

6) **Write your answers as <u>clearly</u> as you can.**
   If the examiner can't read your answer you won't get any marks, even if it's right.

> Obeying these Golden Rules will help you get as many marks as you can in the exam — but they're no use if you haven't learnt the stuff in the first place. So make sure you revise well and do <u>as many</u> practice questions as you can.

Using Your Calculator

1) Your calculator can make questions a lot easier for you but only if you <u>know how to use it</u>. Make sure you know what the different buttons do and how to use them.

2) Remember to check your calculator is in <u>degrees mode</u>. This is important for <u>trigonometry</u> questions.

3) If you're working out a <u>big calculation</u> on your calculator, it's best to do it in <u>stages</u> and use the <u>memory</u> to store the answers to the different parts. If you try and do it all in one go, it's too easy to mess it up.

4) If you're going to be a renegade and do a question all in one go on your calculator, use <u>brackets</u> so the calculator knows which bits to do first.

REMEMBER: <u>Golden Rule number 2</u> still applies, even if you're using a calculator — you should still write down <u>all</u> the steps you are doing so the examiner can see the method you're using.

* = Had to research 3
before answering

Types of Number and BODMAS

1 Use your calculator to work out $\dfrac{197.8}{\sqrt{0.01 + 0.23}}$ 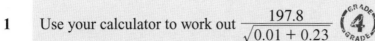 **(4)** GRADE

Give your answer to 2 decimal places.

403.75|75593
403.76

...........*403.76* ✓...........
[Total 2 marks]

2 Use your calculator to work out $\sqrt{\dfrac{12.71 + 137.936}{\cos 50° \times 13.2^2}}$ **(4)** GRADE

Give your answer to 2 decimal places.

1.15|9768003
1.16

...........*1.16* ✓...........
[Total 2 marks]

3 x and y are integers and $0 < x < y$.
Write down two sets of values for x and y such that $6 = \sqrt{3x + 2y}$. **(5)** GRADE

$6 = \sqrt{3x + 2y}$ $x = 4$

$6 = \sqrt{3x + 2y}$ $x = 2$ $6 = \sqrt{3x + 2y}$ $\underline{36}$

$6 = \sqrt{3 \times 2 + 2y}$ $= 36$ $6 = \sqrt{3 \times 4 + 2y}$

$6 = \sqrt{6 + 2 \times 15}$ $y = 15$ $6 = \sqrt{12 + 2y}$ $x = $ ..2.. ✓ , $y = $ ..15.. ✓

$\underline{36}$ $y = 12$ or $x = $ ..4.. ✓ , $y = $ ..12.. ✓

[Total 2 marks]

→ infinite, not an integer

4 Circle the irrational numbers from the list below. **(5)** GRADE

5.5   (π) ✓ 2.5^2 ($\sqrt{3}$) ✓   (0.6π) ✓ $\sqrt{16}$ $\dfrac{7}{9}$

[Total 2 marks]

Score: 8

8

   ✓

Multiples, Factors and Prime Factors

1 Express:

a) 210 as a product of its prime factors.

210
21 ∧ 10
⑦ ③ ⑤ ②

.... $2 \times 3 \times 5 \times 7$ ✓

[2]

b) 105^2 as a product of its prime factors.

105               $5\overline{)105}$ (21)
21 ∧ ⑤
③ ⑦ $3^2 + 5^2 + 7^2$

.... $3^2 + 5^2 + 7^2$ ✓

[2]

[Total 4 marks]

2 Eric says "even square numbers always have more factors than odd square numbers". Find examples to show that Eric is wrong.

even → ④ ⟨1, 4⟩
       2
    less factors

odd → ⑧⑴ ⟨1, 81⟩
   3 27 9
    more factors

.... 4 and 81 ✓

[Total 2 marks]

3 A number, x, is a common multiple of 6 and 7, and a common factor of 252 and 420. Given that $50 < x < 150$, find the value of x.

LCM ↗ 6, 12, 18, 24, 30, 36, ④2, 48, 54, 60, 66, 72, 78, ⑧④, 90, 96, 102
    ↘ 7, 14, 21, 28, 35, ④2, 49, 56, 63, 70, 77, ⑧④, 91, 98

LCM of 6 and 7 → 42, 84

HCF $50 < 84 < 150$

$x = 84$

$x = 84$ ✓

[Total 4 marks]

Score: ☐ 10

10

LCM and HCF

1 $P = 3^7 \times 11^2$ and $Q = 3^4 \times 7^3 \times 11$.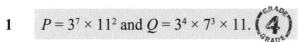

$P = 3^7 \times 11^2$

$Q = 3^4 \times 7^3 \times 11$

 Write as the product of prime factors:

a) the LCM of P and Q,

LCM of P and Q

$3^7 \times 7^3 \times 11^2$ ✓

$[1]$

b) the HCF of P and Q.

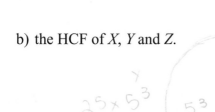

$3^7 \times 11^2$ 3^3 11 11 3^4 3 7^3 $3^4 \times 7^3 \times 11$

$3^4 \times 11$ ✓

$[1]$

[Total 2 marks]

2 $X = 2^8$, $Y = 2^5 \times 5^3$ and $Z = 2^6 \times 5^2 \times 7$.

 Write as the product of prime factors:

a) the LCM of X, Y and Z,

$X = 2^8$

$Y = 2^5 \times 5^3$

$Z = 2^6 \times 5^2 \times 7$

2^3 2^8

$2^8 \times 5^3 \times 7$ ✓

$[2]$

b) the HCF of X, Y and Z.

$2^5 \times 5^3$ 5^3 2^5 5^2 Z $2^6 \times 5^2 \times 7$

2

2^5 ✓

$[2]$

[Total 4 marks]

3 A and B are different prime numbers. Find the LCM of A and B.

$A \times B$ ✓

[Total 2 marks]

Score: 8

8

   ✓

Section One — Number

Fractions

1 Which of these fractions is closest to 1?

$$\frac{5}{6} \qquad \frac{3}{4} \qquad \boxed{\frac{7}{8}} \qquad \frac{4}{5}$$

.... 7/8 √

[Total 1 mark]

2 Work out:

a) $3\frac{1}{2} + 2\frac{3}{5}$

> Make sure each fraction has the same denominator.

$$\frac{7}{2} + \frac{13}{5} = \frac{35}{10} + \frac{26}{10} = \frac{61}{10} = 6\frac{1}{10}$$

.... 6 1/10 √

[3]

b) $3\frac{3}{4} - 2\frac{1}{3}$

$$\frac{15}{4} - \frac{7}{3} = \frac{45}{12} - \frac{28}{12} = \frac{17}{12} = 1\frac{5}{12}$$

.... 1 5/12 √

[3]

[Total 6 marks]

3 Francis owns all the shares of his company.

He sells $\frac{2}{15}$ of the shares to Spencer and $\frac{5}{12}$ of the shares to Jamie.

What fraction of the shares does Francis still own? Give your answer in its simplest form.

15
×12

$$\frac{2}{15} + \frac{5}{12} = \frac{8}{60} + \frac{75}{60} = \frac{33}{60}$$

$$= \frac{11}{20} \quad \rightarrow \boxed{\frac{11}{20}}$$

$$\frac{20}{20} - \frac{11}{20} = \frac{9}{20}$$

.... 9/20 √

[Total 3 marks]

4 Look at shapes X, Y and Z below.

X   Y   Z

$\frac{2}{5}$ of shape X is shaded and $\frac{6}{7}$ of shape Y is shaded.

What fraction of shape Z is shaded?

$$\frac{1}{7} + \frac{2}{5} = \frac{5}{35} + \frac{14}{35} = \frac{19}{35}$$

.... 19/35 √

[Total 3 marks]

Reciprocals

5   If $a = \dfrac{3}{4}$ and $b = 2\dfrac{1}{2}$, find the value of $\dfrac{1}{a} + \dfrac{1}{b}$.

$2\dfrac{1}{2}$

$$\dfrac{3}{4} + \dfrac{5}{2} = \dfrac{6}{8} + \dfrac{20}{8} = \dfrac{26}{64}$$

$a = \dfrac{3}{4}$ $b = 2\dfrac{1}{2}$

$a = \dfrac{3}{4}$ $b = \dfrac{5}{2}$

$$\dfrac{1}{a} + \dfrac{1}{b} = \dfrac{4}{3} + \dfrac{2}{5} = \dfrac{20}{15} + \dfrac{6}{15} = \dfrac{26}{15} = 1\dfrac{11}{15}$$

$\dfrac{13}{32}$ ✗

....

[Total 3 marks]

6   Work out the following, giving your answers as mixed numbers.

 a) $1\dfrac{2}{3} \times \dfrac{9}{10}$

$$\dfrac{5}{3} \times \dfrac{9}{10} = \dfrac{45}{30} = 1\dfrac{15}{30} \qquad 1\dfrac{1}{2}$$

.........$1\dfrac{1}{2}$..✓

[3]

b) $3\dfrac{1}{2} \div 1\dfrac{2}{5}$

$$\dfrac{7}{2} \div \dfrac{7}{5} = \dfrac{7}{2} \times \dfrac{5}{7} = \dfrac{35}{14} = 2\dfrac{7}{14} = 2\dfrac{1}{2} \qquad 2\dfrac{1}{2}✓$$

....

[3]

[Total 6 marks]

7   A factory buys 25 tonnes of flour. $17\dfrac{1}{2}$ tonnes of the flour is used to make scones. $\dfrac{1}{5}$ of the scones are cheese scones.

 a) What fraction of the total amount of flour is used to make cheese scones?

$$17\dfrac{1}{2} \times \dfrac{1}{5} = \dfrac{35}{2} \times \dfrac{1}{5} = \dfrac{35}{10} = \dfrac{7}{2}$$

$$\dfrac{7}{2} \div 25 = \dfrac{7}{50}$$

.........$\dfrac{7}{50}$✓

[2]

b) What percentage of the total amount of flour is used to make cheese scones?

$$\dfrac{7}{50} = \dfrac{14}{100}$$

.........14.....✓.....%

[1]

[Total 3 marks]

Score: 25

25

Fractions and Recurring Decimals

1 Write $\frac{10}{11}$ as a recurring decimal.

.... $0.\dot{9}\dot{0}$ ✓ ....
[Total 1 mark]

✱ **2** Write $\frac{7}{33}$ as a recurring decimal.

$$\frac{7}{33} = \frac{21}{99} \quad = 0.\dot{2}\dot{1}$$

.... $0.\dot{2}\dot{1}$ ✓ ....
[Total 2 marks]

3 Write each of the following in the form $\frac{a}{b}$. Simplify your answers as far as possible.

 a) $0.\dot{7}$ Let r = $0.\dot{7}$ $\overset{\text{Start by naming the decimal.}}{}$

so, 10r = $7.\dot{7}$

10r − r = $7.\dot{7}$ − $0.\dot{7}$

9r = 7

r = $7/9$

$r = \frac{7}{9}$ ✓
[2]

b) $0.\dot{2}\dot{6}$

r = $0.\dot{2}\dot{6}$
10r = $2.\dot{6}\dot{2}$
100r = $26.\dot{2}\dot{6}$
99r = 26
r = 26/99

$r = \frac{26}{99}$ ✓
[2]

c) $1.\dot{3}\dot{6}$

r = $1.\dot{3}\dot{6}$
10r = $13.\dot{6}\dot{3}$
100r = $136.\dot{3}\dot{6}$
99r = 135
r = $\frac{135}{99}$. $\frac{15}{11}$

$r = \frac{15}{11}$ ✓
[3]
[Total 7 marks]

4 Show that $0.5\dot{9}\dot{0} = \frac{13}{22}$

$\overset{\text{Hint: start by trying to get}}{\underset{\text{only the non-repeating part}}{\text{before the decimal point.}}}$

r = $0.5\dot{9}\dot{0}$
10r = $5.\dot{9}\dot{0}$
100r = $59.\dot{0}$
1000r = $590.\dot{9}\dot{0}$
1000r − 10r = 990r = $590.\dot{9}\dot{0}$
                          $5.\dot{9}\dot{0}$
                      ─────────
                          585

990r = 585
r = $\frac{585}{990}$. $\frac{13}{22}$ ✓

[Total 3 marks]

Score: $\boxed{13}$

13

Section One — Number

☹ ☐ ☺ ☐ 😀 ✓

Rounding Numbers and Estimating

1 Look at the following calculation: $\dfrac{215.7 \times 44.8}{460}$

$\dfrac{215.7 \times 44.8}{460}$

a) By rounding each number to 1 significant figure, give an estimate for $\dfrac{215.7 \times 44.8}{460}$.

$$\frac{200 \times 40}{500} = \frac{8000}{500}$$

$$\begin{array}{r} 16 \\ 5\overline{)80} \end{array}$$

$$\frac{80}{5} = 16$$

.................16 ✓.................
[3]

b) Will your answer to part a) be larger or smaller than the exact answer? Explain why.

.....Smaller, because I rounded the original numbers.....

.....down, to find each number to 1 s.f, also I.....

rounded the denominator up, which will [2]

make the result smaller

[Total 5 marks]

2 Work out an estimate for $\sqrt{\dfrac{2321}{19.673 \times 3.81}}$

Show all of your working.

$$= \sqrt{\frac{2000}{20 \times 4}}$$

$$= \sqrt{\frac{2000}{80}}$$

$$\sqrt{\frac{200}{8}} = \sqrt{\frac{100}{4}}$$

$$= \sqrt{25}$$

$$= 5$$

.................5 ✓.................
[Total 3 marks]

3 A cone has a radius (r) of 10 cm, a vertical height (h) of 24 cm and a slant height (l) of 26 cm. Find an estimate for:

 a) The volume of the cone. $\frac{1}{3}\pi r^2 h$

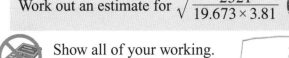
You will need the formulas:
volume = $\frac{1}{3}\pi r^2 h$ and
surface area = $\pi r l + \pi r^2$.

$$\frac{1}{3} \times 3 \times (10^2) \times 20$$

$$\frac{1}{3} \times 3 \times 100 \times 20$$

.............2000 ✓.. cm³
[2]

$$1 \times 100 \times 20$$

b) The surface area of the cone.

$$100 \times 20 = 2000$$

$\pi r l + \pi r^2$

.............1200 ✗.. cm²
?
[2]

$(3 \times 10 \times 30) + (3 \times 10^2)$

2 marks

[Total 4 marks]

$30 \times 30 \qquad 3 \times 100$

$(900) + (300) = 1200$

Score: 10

12

   ✓

Bounds

1 The <u>width</u> of a rectangular piece of paper is 23.6 centimetres, correct to 1 decimal place. The <u>length</u> of the paper is 54.1 centimetres, correct to 1 decimal place.

a) Write down the lower bound for the length of the paper.  **(5)**

$$\frac{1\,dp = 0.5}{2} \qquad 54.05cm$$

..........54.05.......... ✓ cm

[1]

b) Calculate the lower bound for the perimeter of the piece of paper. **(6)**

LB – width → 23.55 cm
LB – length → 54.05 cm

23.55 × 2 = 47.1
54.05 × 2 = 108.1
                155.2 cm

..........155.2.......... ✓ cm

[2]

[Total 3 marks]

2 Here is a rectangle.
$x = 55$ mm to the nearest 5 mm. **(7)**
$y = 30$ mm to the nearest 5 mm.

$\frac{5}{2}$ mm = 2.5 mm

Not to scale

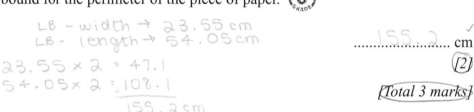

Calculate the upper bound for the area of this rectangle.
Give your answer to 3 significant figures.

$x = 55$ mm → ub = 57.5 mm
$y = 30$ mm → ub = 32.5 mm

57.5 × 32.5 = 1868.75

3.sf = 1870.00

..........1870..........✓ mm²

[Total 3 marks]

3 Given that $x = 2.2$ correct to 1 decimal place, find the interval that **(7)** contains the value of $4x + 3$. Give your answer as an inequality.

....

[Total 4 marks]

4 Samantha is comparing the volume of two buckets. She measures the volume of each bucket to the nearest 0.1 litres and finds that bucket A has a volume of **(7)** 8.3 litres and bucket B has a volume of 13.7 litres.

Calculate the lower bound of the difference, in litres,
between the volumes of bucket A and bucket B

.... litres

[Total 2 marks]

5   Rounded to 1 decimal place, a triangle has a height of 3.2 cm and an area of 5.2 cm².
Calculate the upper bound for the base length of the triangle, giving your answer to 2 d.p.

.... cm
[Total 3 marks]

6   Dan runs 100 m, measured to the nearest metre. His time is 12.5 s to the nearest tenth of a second.

Use the formula below to find Dan's speed to a suitable number of significant figures.
Give a reason for your final answer.

$$\text{speed (m/s)} = \frac{\text{distance (m)}}{\text{time (s)}}$$

lower bound for distance = ... m   upper bound for distance = ... m

upper bound for time = ... s   lower bound for time = ... s

lower bound for speed = $\dfrac{\text{............ m}}{\text{............ s}}$ = ... m/s   upper bound for speed = $\dfrac{\text{............ m}}{\text{............ s}}$ = ... m/s

to 2 s.f. = ... m/s   to 1 s.f. = ... m/s   to 2 s.f. = ... m/s   to 1 s.f. = ... m/s

TIP: compare your upper and lower bounds.

....

....
[Total 5 marks]

7   A cuboid measures 0.94 m by 0.61 m by 0.21 m, each measured to the nearest cm.

0.5 cm

Find the volume of the cuboid in m³ to a suitable degree of accuracy.

0.94 m = 94 cm + 0.5 = 94.5 cm = 0.945 m   0.935 m

0.615 m   0.605 m

0.935 × 0.605 × 0.205 = 0.12 m³   0.215 m   0.205 m

........0.12........ m³
[Total 4 marks]

Exam Practice Tip

If you're stuck in the exam wondering which bounds to use in a calculation, think about what would happen if you used the upper or lower bound for each of the numbers in your calculation. And remember that dividing something by a <u>bigger</u> number gives you a <u>smaller</u> number — and vice versa.

Score

24

Standard Form

1 $A = 4.834 \times 10^9$, $B = 2.7 \times 10^5$, $C = 5.8 \times 10^3$

 a) Express A as an ordinary number.

4.834.000000   4,834,000,000 ✓

[1]

b) Work out $B \times C$. Give your answer in standard form.

$(2.7 \times 10^5) \times (5.8 \times 10^3)$ 1.566 × 10⁹

270,000 × 5800 = 1566000000

1.566 × 10⁹

[2]

c) Put A, B and C in order from smallest to largest.

5.8×10^3, 2.7×10^5, 4.834×10^9 ✓

[1]

[Total 4 marks]

2 Light travels at approximately 1.86×10^5 miles per second.
The distance from the Earth to the Sun is approximately 9.3×10^7 miles.

How long will it take light to travel this distance?
Give your answer in standard form.

$\dfrac{9.3 \times 10^7}{1.86 \times 10^5}$ = 5×10^2

5×10^2 seconds

[Total 2 marks]

3 $A = (5 \times 10^5) + (5 \times 10^3) + (5 \times 10^2) + (5 \times 10^{-2})$

Find the value of A. Give your answer as an ordinary number

$(500 \times 10^3) + (5 \times 10^3)$ $(5 \times 10^2) + (0.05 \times 10^2)$

$(500 + 5) \times 10^3$

505×10^3

5.05×10^5

....

[Total 2 marks]

4 The distance from Neptune to the Sun is approximately 4.5×10^9 km.
The distance from the Earth to the Sun is approximately 1.5×10^8 km.

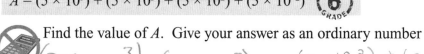 Calculate the ratio of the Earth-Sun distance to the Neptune-Sun distance.
Give your answer in the form $1 : n$.

....

[Total 3 marks]

5 A patient has been prescribed a dose of 4×10^{-4} grams of a certain drug to be given daily.

a) The tablets that the hospital stocks each contain 8×10^{-5} grams of the drug.
How many tablets should the patient be given each day?

$$\frac{4 \times 10^{-4}}{8 \times 10^{-5}} =$$

.... tablets

[3]

b) The doctor increases the patient's daily dose of the drug by 6×10^{-5} grams.
What is the patient's new daily dose of the drug?

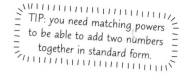

TIP: you need matching powers to be able to add two numbers together in standard form.

$$\frac{4 \times 10^{-4} + 6 \times 10^{-5}}{8 \times 10^{-5}}$$

.... grams per day

[3]

[Total 6 marks]

6 A cruise ship weighs approximately 7.59×10^{7} kg.
Its passengers weigh a total of 2.1×10^{5} kg.

Express the weight of the passengers as a percentage of the total combined
weight of the ship and passengers. Give your answer to 2 decimal places.

.... %

[Total 3 marks]

7 Express $\dfrac{3^{2}}{2^{122} \times 5^{120}}$ in standard form.

$$\frac{3^{2}}{2^{122} \times 5^{120}} = \frac{9}{2^{......}(2^{......} \times 5^{120})}$$

$$= \frac{........}{........ \times 10^{......}}$$

$$= \frac{........}{........} \times \frac{1}{10^{......}}$$

$$= .... \times 10^{......}$$

[Total 2 marks]

Score: [ ]

22

Section One — Number

Section Two — Algebra

Algebra Basics

1 Leah is tiling a section of her bathroom wall.
The tiles are a cm wide and b cm tall and she needs 20 tiles in total.

Find an expression for the area of the wall she is tiling in terms of a and b.

..........20ab.......... $\overset{\checkmark}{}$ cm²

[Total 1 mark]

2 On the diagram below, shade the area represented by $pq + 3pr$.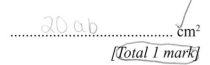

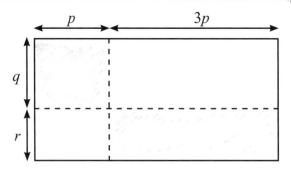

$\checkmark$

[Total 1 mark]

3 Peter is making a sculpture using different pieces of metal tubing.
He makes a tower by stacking 7 pieces that are $(f + g)$ cm tall, 9 pieces
that are $(h - g)$ cm tall and 5 pieces that are $2h$ cm tall on top of each other.

Find a simplified expression for the height of the tower in terms of f, g and h.

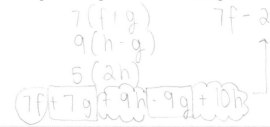

..........7f - 2g + 19h.......... $\checkmark$ cm

[Total 2 marks]

4 The diagram below shows a rectangle with sides that are $4x + 3$ cm and $5x - 9$ cm long.

Find an expression in terms of x for the
side length of a regular hexagon with the
same perimeter as the rectangle.

$5x - 9$ cm

$4x + 3$ cm

Diagram not
accurately drawn

$2(5x - 9) = 10x - 18$

$2(4x + 3) = 8x + 6$

$\overline{\hspace{2cm}}$

$18x - 12$

..........3x - 2.......... $\checkmark$ cm

[Total 3 marks]

$18x - 12 \div 6 = 3x - 2$

Score: $\boxed{7}$

$\overline{7}$

Powers and Roots

1 Circle the correct value of 5^{-2}.

$\dfrac{1}{5^2} = \dfrac{1}{25}$

  -25 2.5 $\dfrac{2}{5}$ $\boxed{\dfrac{1}{25}}$ ✓ $\sqrt{5}$

[Total 1 mark]

2 Show that $8^{\frac{4}{3}} = 16$.

$8^{\frac{1}{3}} = \sqrt[3]{8} = 2$ $8^{\frac{4}{3}} = 16$

$8^{\frac{4}{3}} = (8^{\frac{1}{3}})^4 = (\underline{\ 2\ })^4 = \underline{\ 16\ }$ ✓

[Total 2 marks]

3 For values of $y \geq 2$, write the following expressions in order from smallest to largest.

y^{-3} y^3 y^1 y^0 $y^{\frac{1}{3}}$

$\dfrac{1}{y^3}$ $y \times y \times y$ y 1 $\sqrt[3]{y}$?

$\underline{\ y^{-3}\ }, \underline{\ y^0\ }, \underline{\ y^{\frac{1}{3}}\ }, \underline{\ y^1\ }, \underline{\ y^3\ }$

[Total 2 marks]

4 Estimate the value of each of the following to 1 decimal place:

a) x, where $x = \sqrt{70}$

$x = 8.366600265$
$x = 8.4$

$\underline{\ 8.4\ }$ ✓
[2]

b) y, where $3^y = 20$

$3^y = 20$
$y = 2.714417617$

$\underline{\ 2.7\ }$ ✓
[2]

[Total 4 marks]

5 Completely simplify the expression below.

$3y^2 \times \dfrac{b}{3a^2}$

$(9a^4)^{\frac{1}{2}} \times \dfrac{2ab^2}{6a^3b}$

$= (9a^4)^{\frac{1}{2}} \times \dfrac{2ab^2}{6a^3b}$

$= (9a^4)^{\frac{1}{2}} \times \dfrac{2b}{6a^2} = (9a^4)^{\frac{1}{2}} \times \dfrac{b}{3a^2}$

$\underline{\ b\ }$ ✓

[Total 3 marks]

$(9a^4)^{\frac{1}{2}} = \sqrt{9a^4} = 3a^2$

Score: $\boxed{10}$
___
12

Multiplying Out Brackets

1 Expand the brackets in the following expressions.
Simplify your answers as much as possible.

 a) $5p(6 - 2p)$ $30p \cdot 10p^2$

.............$30p - 10p^2$ ✓

[2]

b) $(2t - 5)(3t + 4)$

$6t^2 + 8t - 15t - 20$

$= 6t^2 - 7t - 20$

.............$6t^2 - 7t - 20$ ✓

[2]

[Total 4 marks]

2 a, b and c are integers such that $4(5x - 7) + 6(4 - 2x) = a(bx + c)$, and $a > 0$. Find the values of a, b and c.

$4(5x - 7) = 20x - 28$

$6(4 - 2x) = 24 - 12x$

$20x - 28 + 24 - 12x$

$8x - 4 = 4(2x - 1)$

$a = \underline{\ 4\ }$ ✓, $b = \underline{\ 2\ }$ ✓, $c = \underline{\ -1\ }$ ✓

[Total 3 marks]

3 Write an expression for the area of the triangle below. Simplify your expression as much as possible.

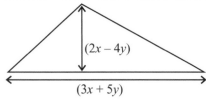

$(2x - 4y)$

$(3x + 5y)$

Diagram not accurately drawn

$\dfrac{(2x - 4y)(3x + 5y)}{2}$

$(2x - 4y)(3x + 5y)$

$\dfrac{6x^2 + 10xy - 12yx - 20y^2}{2}$

.............$3x^2 - 4yx - 10y^2$ ✓

$= 3x^2 + 5xy - 6yx - 10y^2$

$= 3x^2 - yx - 10y^2$

[Total 3 marks]

4 Expand and simplify $(x - 1)(2x + 3)(2x - 3)$.

$(x - 1) \times (2x + 3)(2x - 3)$

$4x^2 - 6x + 6x - 9$

$= 4x^2 - 9$

$(x - 1)(4x^2 - 9)$

$= 4x^3 - 9x - 4x^2 + 9$

$= 4x^3$

.............$4x^3 - 9x - 4x^2 + 9$ ✓

[Total 3 marks]

Exam Practice Tip

If you're struggling with double brackets in the exam, don't forget you can always use the <u>FOIL</u> method — multiply the <u>F</u>irst term in each bracket together, then multiply the <u>O</u>utside terms together, then the <u>I</u>nside terms, and finally multiply together the <u>L</u>ast term in each bracket... easy.

Score

13

13

Factorising

1 Factorise the following expressions fully.

 a) $7y - 21y^2$

$7y(1 - 3y)$

.............$7y(1-3y)$ ✓
[2]

b) $2v^3w + 8v^2w^2$

$2v^2w(v + 4w)$

.............$2v^2w(v+4w)$ ✓
[2]

[Total 4 marks]

2 Factorise the following expressions fully.

 a) $x^2 - 16$

$(x+4)(x-4)$

.............$(x+4)(x-4)$ ✓
[1]

✻ b) $9n^2 - 4m^2$

$(3n-2m)(3n+2m)$

.............$(3n-2m)(3n+2m)$ ✓
[2]

✻ c) $3y^2 - 15$

$3(y^2 - 5)$
$3(y^2 - (\sqrt{5})^2)$
$= 3(y + \sqrt{5})(y - \sqrt{5})$

.............$3(y+\sqrt{5})(y-\sqrt{5})$ ✓
[2]

[Total 5 marks]

3 ✻ Fully factorise $x^3 - 25x$.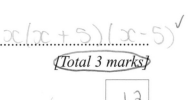

$x(x + 5)(x - 5)$
$(x^2 + 5x)(x - 5)$

$x^3 - 5x^2 + 5x^2 - 25x$

$x^3 - 25x$

.............$x(x+5)(x-5)$ ✓

[Total 3 marks]

Score: 12

12

  ✓

Section Two — Algebra

18

Manipulating Surds

1 Write $(2 + \sqrt{3})(5 - \sqrt{3})$ in the form $a + b\sqrt{3}$, where a and b are integers.

$(2 + \sqrt{3})(5 - \sqrt{3})$

$10 - 2\sqrt{3} + 5\sqrt{3} - 3$

$7 + 3\sqrt{3}$

.... $7 + 3\sqrt{3}$ ✓ ......

[Total 2 marks]

2 Write $2\sqrt{50} - (\sqrt{2})^3$ in the form $a\sqrt{b}$, where a and b are integers.

$2\sqrt{50} - (\sqrt{2})^3$

$\sqrt{2} \times \sqrt{2} \times \sqrt{2} = 2\sqrt{2}$

$2\sqrt{50}$

$\sqrt{25}\sqrt{2}$

$2 \times \sqrt{2} = 2\sqrt{2}$

5

$= 10\sqrt{2}$

$10\sqrt{2} - 2\sqrt{2} = 8\sqrt{2}$

.... $8\sqrt{2}$ ✓ ......

[Total 2 marks]

3 Express $\sqrt{396} + \dfrac{22}{\sqrt{11}} - \dfrac{220}{\sqrt{44}}$ in the form $a\sqrt{11}$, where a is an integer.

....

[Total 4 marks]

4 Express $\dfrac{1 + \sqrt{7}}{3 - \sqrt{7}}$ in the form $a + b\sqrt{7}$, where a and b are integers.

Multiply by $3 + \sqrt{7}$ to rationalise the denominator.

....

[Total 4 marks]

Score:

12

Solving Equations

1 Poppy, Felix and Alexi sell 700 raffle tickets between them.
Poppy sells twice as many tickets as Felix, and Alexi sells 25 more tickets than Poppy.

How many tickets did each of them sell?

$F = x$
$P = 2x$
$A = 2x + 25$

$2x + 25 + 2x + x$
$5x + 25 = 700$
-25
$5x = 675$
$x = 135$

$F = 135$
$P = 2 \times 135$
$A = (2 \times 135) + 25$

Poppy .....270..... ✓
Felix .....135..... ✓
Alexi .....295..... ✓

[Total 5 marks]

2 The diagram below shows an equilateral triangle.

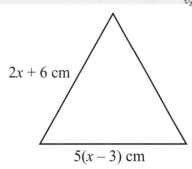

$2x + 6$ cm

$5(x - 3)$ cm

Find the length of one side of the equilateral triangle.

$2x + 6 = 5(x - 3)$
$2x + 6 = 5x - 15$
$+15 \qquad +15$
$2x + 21 = 5x$
$-2x \qquad -2x$
$21 = 3x$
$7 = x$

$2x + 6$ cm $\qquad x = 7$
$2(7) + 6$ cm
$14 + 6$ cm
20 cm

.....20..... ✓ cm

[Total 4 marks]

3 Solve the equation $\frac{5}{4}(2c - 1) = 3c - 2$

$\frac{5}{4}(2c - 1) = 3c - 2$
$\times 4$
$5(2c - 1) = 4(3c - 2)$
$10c - 5 = 12c - 8$
$-10c$
$-5 = 2c - 8$
$+8$
$3 = 2c$

$2c = 3$
$c = \frac{3}{2}$

$c = ...\frac{3}{2}..... ✓$

[Total 3 marks]

Section Two — Algebra

4 Liam and Neil want to buy a new games console, which costs £360.
They both get weekend jobs, where they each get paid £4.50 per hour.
When they can afford the games console, Liam has worked 30 more hours than Neil.

How many hours did each boy work?

$$450(x) + 450(x+30) = 360$$
$$4.5x + 4.5x + 13500 = 360$$

Neil: x
Liam: $x + 30$

Liam: .... hours, Neil: .... hours

[Total 3 marks]

5 Solve the following equations.

a) $5x^2 = 180$

$$\begin{array}{r} 36 \\ 5\sqrt{180} \end{array}$$

$$5 \times x^2 = 180$$
$$\div 5$$
$$x^2 = 36 \quad x = 6$$

$x = \overset{+}{\underset{-}{}} 6$ ✓

[2]

b) $\dfrac{8 - 2x}{3} + \dfrac{2x + 4}{9} = 12$

$$\frac{8-2x}{3} + \frac{2x+4}{9} = \frac{24-6x}{9} + \frac{2x+4}{9} = \frac{28--4x}{9} = 12$$

$$\frac{28-4x}{9} = 12 \qquad 28 - 4x = 108$$
$$\times 9 \qquad\qquad\qquad -28$$
$$-4x = 80 \qquad x = -20$$

$x = -20$

[4]

[Total 6 marks]

6 Hassan thinks of two different positive integers.
Their product is 147, and one number is three times the other number.

What are the two numbers Hassan is thinking of?

$$3x \times \overset{y}{x} = 147$$

....

[Total 3 marks]

Exam Practice Tip

It's a good idea to check your solutions by substituting them back into the equation and checking that everything works out properly. If the unknown appears on both sides of the equation, make sure you work out the value on each side. It certainly beats sitting and twiddling your thumbs or counting sheep to kill time.

Score

24

Section Two — Algebra

Formulas

1 Neela is on holiday in New York. The local weather forecast says that the temperature tomorrow will be 41 °F. Neela wants to know what this temperature is in °C.

The formula for converting temperatures in °C to °F is: $F = \frac{9}{5}C + 32$.

a) Rearrange the formula to make C the subject.

$$F = \frac{9}{5}C + 32$$
$$\quad\quad -32$$
$$F - 32 = \frac{9}{5}C$$

$$\frac{F - 32}{1.8} = C$$

$$C = \frac{F - 32}{1.8}$$

[2]

b) What will the temperature be in New York tomorrow in °C?

$$C = \frac{41 - 32}{1.8}$$

$$C = 5$$

......5...... °C

[2]

[Total 4 marks]

2 A result used in physics is $P = \frac{V^2}{R}$, where P is the power in watts (W), V is the voltage in volts (V) and R is the resistance in ohms (Ω).

a) Calculate the power of an electrical circuit with a voltage of 12 V and a resistance of 16 Ω.

.... W

[1]

b) In a different circuit, the power is 25W when the voltage is 20V.
Find the resistance in ohms.

.... Ω

[2]

[Total 3 marks]

3 The formula for the displacement, s, of a dropped object in free fall is $s = \frac{1}{2}gt^2$, where g is the constant acceleration due to gravity and t is time taken.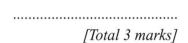

Rearrange the formula to make t the subject.

....

[Total 3 marks]

Section Two — Algebra

4 The relationship between a, b and y is given by the formula $a + y = \dfrac{b - y}{a}$.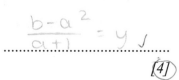

 a) Rearrange this formula to make y the subject.

$a + y = \dfrac{b + y}{\times a \quad a}$

$a(a + y) = b - y$

$a^2 + ay = b - y \quad + y$

$a^2 + ay + y = b'$

$\quad - a^2$

$b - a^2 = ay + y$

$b - a^2 = y(a + 1)$

$\dfrac{b - a^2}{a + 1} = y \checkmark$

[4]

b) Find the value of y when $a = 3$ and $b = 6$.

$\dfrac{b - a^2}{a + 1} = y \qquad \begin{array}{l} a = 3 \\ b = 6 \end{array}$

$\dfrac{6 - 3^2}{3 + 1} = y \qquad \dfrac{6 - 9}{4} = y \qquad \dfrac{-3}{4} = y$

$\dfrac{b - a^2}{a + 1} = y$

$y = \underline{-0.75}\checkmark$

[1]

[Total 5 marks]

5 Rearrange the formula below to make n the subject.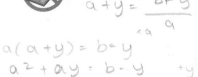

$$x = \sqrt{\dfrac{(1 + n)}{(1 - n)}}$$

....

[Total 5 marks]

6 $x = \dfrac{1 - y}{x}$, where $x > 1$. Decide whether y is positive or negative.

....

[Total 3 marks]

7 $b = \sqrt{2a - 1}$ and $c = 2b^4 + 4b^2$.

Find a formula for a in terms of c.

> Start by finding b^2
> and b^4 in terms of a.

....

[Total 4 marks]

Score:

27

Section Two — Algebra

Factorising Quadratics

1   The product of two consecutive positive even numbers is 288.
By forming and solving an equation, find the larger of the two numbers.

$$2n \ , \ 2n+2$$

$$(2n)\times(2n+2)$$
$$4n^2 + 4n = 288$$

....
[Total 4 marks]

2   The expression $5x^2 - 19x + 18$ is an example of a quadratic expression.

$\frac{18}{5 \times 18}$ $\frac{\times 5}{90}$ + $\begin{array}{c} F \ of \ 90 \\ -10, -9 \end{array}$

   a) Fully factorise the expression $5x^2 - 19x + 18$.

$$5x^2 - 10x - 9x + 18$$
$$5x(x-2) - 9(x-2)$$
$$(5x-9)(x-2)$$

........$(5x-9)(x-2)$
[2]

b) Use your answer to part a) to factorise the expression $5(x-1)^2 - 19(x-1) + 18$.

....
[2]
[Total 4 marks]

3   The shape on the right is made from a square and a triangle.

The sides of the square are $(x + 3)$ cm long
and the height of the triangle is $(2x + 2)$ cm.
The area of the whole shape is 60 cm².

Find the value of x.

> *Don't forget, a length
> can't have a negative value.*

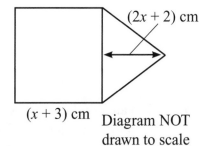

$(x + 3)$ cm Diagram NOT
drawn to scale

Square:

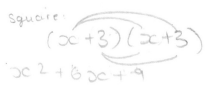
$(x+3)(x+3)$
$x^2 + 6x + 9$

Triangle: $(2x+2)(x+3)$

$2x^2 + 6x + 2x + 6$

$2x^2 + 8x + 6$ $\div 2$

$x^2 + 4x + 3$

Square + Triangle:

$x^2 + 6x + 9 + x^2 + 4x + 3$

$2x^2 + 10x + 12 = 60 \, cm^2$

$\qquad\qquad -60$

$2x^2 + 10x - 48 = 0$

$x^2 + 5x - 24 = 0$

$(x-3)(x+8) = 0$ F of -24

$x = 3$ $-8, 3$
$x = -8$ $-3, 8$

$x = $ ....3..... or -8 ✓

[Total 7 marks]

Score:

15

The Quadratic Formula

1 Solve the quadratic equation $x^2 + 5x + 3 = 0$, giving your answers to 2 decimal places.

$a = \underline{1}$, $b = \underline{5}$ and $c = \underline{3}$

$$x = \frac{-b \pm \sqrt{b^2 - 4ac}}{2a} = \frac{-\underline{5} \pm \sqrt{\underline{5}^2 - (4 \times \underline{1} \times \underline{3})}}{2 \times \underline{1}} = \frac{-\underline{5} \pm \sqrt{\underline{13}}}{\underline{2}}$$

$$\begin{array}{r} 25 \\ -12 \\ \hline 13 \end{array}$$

$25 - 12$

$x = \underline{^-0.70}$ or $x = \underline{^-4.30}$

[Total 3 marks]

2 Solve the equation $2x^2 - 7x + 2 = 0$. Give your answers correct to 2 decimal places.

$x = \dfrac{^-b \pm \sqrt{b^2 - 4ac}}{2a}$ $\begin{array}{l} a = 2 \\ b = ^-7 \\ c = 2 \end{array}$ $x = \dfrac{7 \pm \sqrt{33}}{4}$

$x = \dfrac{^-(^-7) \pm \sqrt{(^-7^2) - (4 \times 2 \times 2)}}{2 \times 2}$ $\begin{array}{l} +x = \\ -x = \end{array}$

$x = \dfrac{7 \pm \sqrt{49 - (16)}}{4}$ $\begin{array}{r} 49 \\ -16 \\ \hline 33 \end{array}$ $x = \underline{3.19}$ or $x = \underline{0.31}$

[Total 3 marks]

3 Solve the equation $3x^2 - 2x - 4 = 0$. Give your answers in simplified surd form.

$x = \dfrac{^-b \pm \sqrt{b^2 - 4ac}}{2a}$ $\begin{array}{l} a = 3 \\ b = ^-2 \\ c = ^-4 \end{array}$ $x = \dfrac{2 \pm \sqrt{52}}{6}$

$x = \dfrac{^-(^-2) \pm \sqrt{(^-2)^2 - (4 \times 3 \times ^-4)}}{2 \times 3}$ $+x = 0.$ $x = \dfrac{1 \pm \sqrt{13}}{6}$ $-x =$

$x = \dfrac{2 \pm \sqrt{4 - (^-48}}{6}$ $x = \underline{\dfrac{1 + \sqrt{13}}{6}}$ or $x = \underline{\dfrac{1 - \sqrt{13}}{6}}$

[Total 3 marks]

4 The area of the rectangle on the right is 30 cm².
Find the exact length of the longer side of the rectangle.

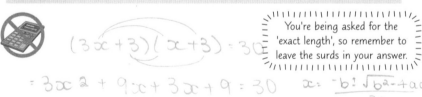
You're being asked for the 'exact length', so remember to leave the surds in your answer.

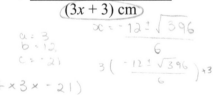

$(3x + 3)(x + 3) = 30$

$= 3x^2 + 9x + 3x + 9 = 30$

$= 3x^2 + 12x + 9 = 30$

-9

$= 3x^2 + 12x = 21$

$= 3x^2 + 12x - 21 = 0$

$x = \dfrac{^-b \pm \sqrt{b^2 - 4ac}}{2a}$ $\begin{array}{l} a = 3 \\ b = 12 \\ c = ^-21 \end{array}$

$x = \dfrac{^-12 \pm \sqrt{12^2 - (4 \times 3 \times ^-21)}}{2 \times 3}$

$x = \dfrac{^-12 \pm \sqrt{144 - (^-252)}}{6}$

$x = \dfrac{^-12 \pm \sqrt{396}}{6}$

$3\left(\dfrac{^-12 \pm \sqrt{396}}{6}\right) + 3$

$\begin{array}{r} 12 \\ \times 21 \\ \hline 12 \\ 24 \\ \hline 252 \end{array}$ $\begin{array}{r} 252 \\ -144 \\ \hline 396 \end{array}$

$\underline{\hspace{3cm}}$ cm

[Total 5 marks]

Exam Practice Tip

One thing you really need to watch out for when it comes to using the quadratic formula are those pesky minus signs — especially if a, b or c are negative. Just take your time when you're putting them into the formula — you don't want to throw away easy marks simply because you've messed up your minuses.

Score

14

Section Two — Algebra

Completing the Square

1 Given that $x^2 + ax + b = (x + 2)^2 - 9$, work out the values of a and b.

$(x + 2)^2 - 9$

$(x + 2)(x + 2) = x^2 + 4x + 4 - 9$

$= x^2 + 4x - 5$

$a = \underline{4}$ ✓ and $b = \underline{-5}$ ✓

[Total 2 marks]

2 The expression $x^2 - 10x - 5$ can be written in the form $(x + p)^2 + q$.

 a) Find the values of p and q.

$x^2 - 10x - 5$

$\downarrow \div 2$

$(x - 5)^2 - 30$

$(x - 5)(x - 5) = x^2 - 5x - 5x + 25 = x^2 - 10x + 25$

$(x - 5)^2 = 30$

$p = \underline{-5}$ ✓ and $q = \underline{-30}$ ✓

[3]

b) Use your answer to solve the equation $x^2 - 10x - 5 = 0$.
   Leave your answer in surd form.

$x = \dots\dots\dots$ or $x = \dots\dots\dots$

[2]

[Total 5 marks]

3 A curve has equation $y = 2x^2 - 8x + 19$.

a) Write the expression $2x^2 - 8x + 19$ in the form $a(x + b)^2 + c$.

$\dots\dots\dots\dots\dots\dots\dots$

[4]

b) Find the coordinates of the minimum point of the graph. $\leftarrow$ complete the square

$\dots\dots\dots\dots\dots\dots\dots$

[1]

c) State if and where the graph of the equation crosses the x-axis.

> Think about the minimum
> value of the graph.

$\dots\dots\dots\dots\dots\dots\dots$

[1]

[Total 6 marks]

Exam Practice Tip

Completing the square is pretty tough stuff. If you're struggling to get your head around it, just remember...
when the quadratic expression is in the form $x^2 + bx + c$, the number in the brackets is always $b \div 2$ and the
number outside the brackets is always $c - (b \div 2)^2$.

Score

13

Algebraic Fractions

1 Simplify the algebraic fraction below as much as possible.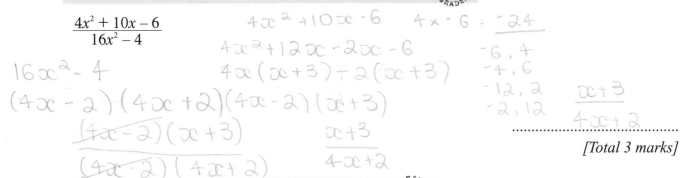

$$\frac{4x^2 + 10x - 6}{16x^2 - 4}$$

$16x^2 - 4$

$(4x - 2)(4x + 2)$

$\dfrac{(4x - 2)(x + 3)}{(4x - 2)(4x + 2)}$

$4x^2 + 10x - 6$

$4x^2 + 12x - 2x - 6$

$4x(x + 3) - 2(x + 3)$

$(4x - 2)(x + 3)$

$\dfrac{x + 3}{4x + 2}$

$4x - 6 = -24$

$-6, 4$
$-4, 6$
$-12, 2$
$-2, 12$

$\dfrac{x + 3}{4x + 2}$

....

[Total 3 marks]

2 Simplify the calculation below as much as possible.

$$\frac{2a - 8}{a^2 - 9} \div \frac{a^2 - 2a - 8}{a^2 + 5a + 6} \times (2a^2 - a - 15)$$

$2a^3 - 8a^2$

$\dfrac{2a - 8}{a^2 - 9} \times \dfrac{a^2 + 5a + 6}{a^2 - 2a - 8} \times (2a^2 - a - 15)$

$\dfrac{(a^2 + 5a + 6)(2a - 8)}{(a^2 - 2a - 8)(a^2 - 9)} \times (2a^2 - a - 15)$

....

[Total 5 marks]

3 Write $\dfrac{2}{3} + \dfrac{m - 2n}{m + 3n}$ as a single fraction.

$\dfrac{2}{3} + \dfrac{m - 2n}{m + 3n} = \dfrac{2 \times ....}{3 \times ....} + \dfrac{........ \times (m - 2n)}{........ \times (m + 3n)} = \dfrac{2................ + ... (m - 2n)}{......... (m + 3n)}$

$= \dfrac{\text{................}}{\text{................}} = \dfrac{\text{................}}{\text{................}}$

$\dfrac{2}{3} + \dfrac{m - 2n}{m + 3n}$ $\dfrac{2(m + 3n)}{3(m + 3n)} + \dfrac{2(3)}{3(m + 3n)} = \dfrac{2m + 3n + 6}{3(m + 3n)}$

....

[Total 3 marks]

4 Write $\dfrac{1}{x - 5} + \dfrac{2}{x - 2}$ as a single fraction.

$\dfrac{1}{x - 5} + \dfrac{2}{x - 2}$

....

[Total 3 marks]

Score: ☐

14

Sequences

1 The first four terms in a sequence are 3, 8, 13, 18, ...

a) Find the *n*th term of the sequence. **(4)**

.... 5n - 2 ....

[2]

b) Using your answer to part a), find an expression for the product of the *n*th and (*n* + 1)th **(6)** terms of the sequence. Simplify your answer as much as possible.

....

[2]

[Total 4 marks]

2 This question is about the sequence 3, 7, 11, 15, 19... **(4)**

a) Find the *n*th term of the sequence.

.... 4n - 1 ✓ ....

[2]

b) Explain why 502 cannot be a term in this sequence.

Because 502 + 1 = 503 and 503 ÷ 4 is not an integer so it is not a term in this sequence.

[2]

[Total 4 marks]

3 The first four terms in a sequence are $\sqrt{2}$, 2, $2\sqrt{2}$, 4... **(5)**

a) Find the next two terms in the sequence.

....

[2]

b) Circle the expression for the *n*th term of the sequence.

$\sqrt{2n}$ $n\sqrt{2}$ $(\sqrt{2})^n$ $n(\sqrt{2})^2$

[1]

[Total 3 marks]

4 The term-to-term rule of a sequence is $u_{n+1} = 2u_n + 1$. **(5)**

a) If $u_1 = 0.5$, find the values of the next two terms in the sequence.

....
[2]

b) A different sequence has the same term-to-term rule, but $u_1 = 1.5$. Find u_2, u_3 and u_4.

....
[3]

c) What do you notice if you start with $u_1 = -1$?

....
[1]

[Total 6 marks]

5 A quadratic sequence begins 2, 6, 12, 20, ... **(7)**

a) Write down the next term in the sequence.

2, 6, 12, 20

4 6 8 10

2 2

$n^2 + n$

...............30n...............
[2]

b) Find an expression for the *n*th term of the sequence.

...............$n^2 + n$...............
[3]

[Total 5 marks]

Section Two — Algebra

6 The term-to-term rule of a sequence is $u_{n+1} = \dfrac{-1}{2u_n}$. **⑤**

a) If $u_1 = 2$, find the values of the next three terms in the sequence.

....
[2]

b) Write down the value of u_{50}.

....
[1]

[Total 3 marks]

7 The patterns below are made up of grey and white squares.

Pattern 1   Pattern 2   Pattern 3   Pattern 4

a) Find an expression for the number of **grey** squares in the nth pattern. **④**

....
[2]

b) Giles makes two consecutive patterns in the sequence. **⑥**
He uses 414 grey squares in total. Which 2 patterns has he made?

....
[3]

c) Find an expression for the **total** number of squares in the nth pattern. **⑦**

....
[3]

[Total 8 marks]

Exam Practice Tip

Sequence questions are all about spotting the pattern — don't be put off if it's one you haven't come across before (examiners like to try and catch you off guard by throwing in things like roots and fractions). You might even come across a sequence where a numerator and denominator each follow a different rule.

Score

33

Section Two — Algebra

Inequalities

1 Circle the inequality that is shown on the number line below.

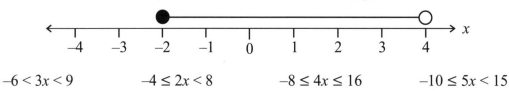

$$-6 < 3x < 9 \qquad -4 \le 2x < 8 \qquad -8 \le 4x \le 16 \qquad -10 \le 5x < 15$$

[Total 1 mark]

2 Solve the inequality $4x + 1 > x - 5$.

$$4x + 1 > x - 5$$
$$\qquad\qquad +5$$
$$4x + 6 > x$$
$$-4x$$
$$\qquad 6 > {}^{-}3x$$

....

[Total 2 marks]

3 Find the integer values that satisfy both of the following inequalities:

$5n - 3 \le 17$ and $2n + 6 > 8$

Give your answer using set notation.

....

[Total 3 marks]

4 Find the largest three consecutive even numbers that sum to less than 1000.

....

[Total 3 marks]

5 Solve the following inequalities.

 a) $5x^2 < 80$

$$x^2 < 16 \qquad x < \sqrt{16} \qquad x < 4$$

.... $x < 4$ ....

[3]

b) $x^2 + 1 < x + 7$

$$x^2 + 1 < x + 7$$
$$\qquad -1$$
$$x^2 < x + 6$$
$$\qquad -x$$
$$x^2 - x < 6$$

....

[3]

[Total 6 marks]

Score:

15

Section Two — Algebra

Graphical Inequalities

1 Look at the grid below.

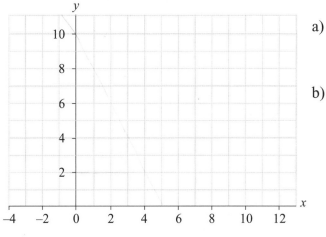

$y = mx + c$
$y = -2x + 10$

a) Use the grid to draw the graphs of $2x + y = 10$ and $y = x + 2$.

[2]

b) Shade and label, using the letter S, the area represented by the inequalities $x \geq 1$, $2x + y \leq 10$, $y \geq x + 2$.

[2]

[Total 4 marks]

2 Look at the grid on the right.

On the grid, shade the region that represents these inequalities:
$x < 5$
$y \geq -2$
$y - x \leq 1$

$y - x = 1$
$\quad + x$
$y = x + 1$ ✓

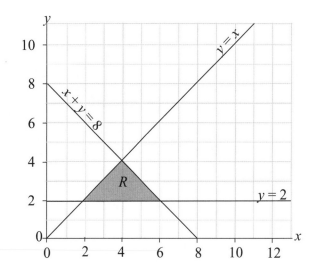

[Total 4 marks]

3 Look at the grid on the right.

The shaded region R is bounded by the lines $y = 2$, $y = x$ and $x + y = 8$.

Write down three inequalities which define R.

....

....

....

[Total 3 marks]

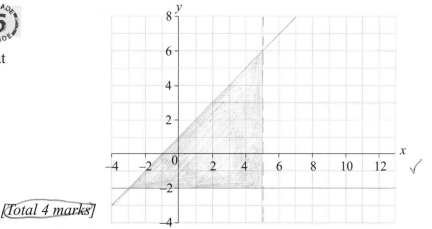

Exam Practice Tip

You need to pay close attention to whether the symbol is just < or > or whether it's ≤ or ≥. If it's < or >, draw a dashed line on the graph. If it's ≤ or ≥ you need to use a solid line. If you're not sure which side of the line you want, pick a point with coordinates that satisfy the inequality and see which side of the line it lies.

Score

11

Section Two — Algebra

Iterative Methods

1 The equation $x^3 - 4x + 2 = 0$ has a solution between $x = -2$ and $x = -3$.

By filling in the table below, find an approximation to the solution of $x^3 - 4x + 2 = 0$ to 1 d.p.
You might not need to use all the rows.

x	$x^3 - 4x + 2$	
−2	2	Positive ✓
−3	−17 ✓	Negative
−2.1	1.139	Positive ✓
−2.2	0.152 ✓	Positive

$-8 - 4(-2) + 2 = -8 + 8 + 2$

$-27 - 4(-2) + 2 = -27 + 8 + 2$

$x = ...$

[Total 4 marks]

2 Use the iteration machine below with a starting value of $x_0 = 1$
to find an approximation to the solution of $5x^3 + 3x - 6 = 0$ to 5 d.p.

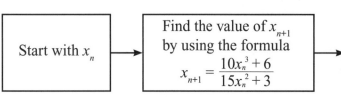

| Start with x_n | → | Find the value of x_{n+1} by using the formula $$x_{n+1} = \frac{10x_n^3 + 6}{15x_n^2 + 3}$$ | → | If $x_{n+1} = x_n$ when rounded to 5 d.p. then stop. If $x_{n+1} \neq x_n$ when rounded to 5 d.p. start again using x_{n+1}. |

Type in '1 =' on your calculator. Now, if you enter (10ans³ + 6) ÷ (15ans² + 3) and keep pressing '=', you'll get the values of x_1, x_2 etc. without having to put the calculation in again.

$x = ...$

[Total 3 marks]

3 The equation $3x - 2x^3 + 5 = 0$ has one solution.

a) Show that this solution lies in the interval $1.5 < x < 2$.

[2]

b) Show that $3x - 2x^3 + 5 = 0$ can be written as:

$$x = \sqrt[3]{\frac{3x + 5}{2}}$$

[3]

c) Use the iteration $x_{n+1} = \sqrt[3]{\frac{3x_n + 5}{2}}$ to find the solution to $3x - 2x^3 + 5 = 0$ to 5 d.p.
Use a starting value of $x_0 = 2$.

$x =$ ....

[3]

[Total 8 marks]

Exam Practice Tip

Don't panic — the exam questions will guide you through the iteration and tell you which method to use.
It wouldn't just say 'use iteration to find the solution to this equation' as that would just be mean.
Be careful with decimal places — you might have to find a root to 2, 3, 4 or even 5 d.p.

Score

15

Simultaneous Equations

1   Solve this pair of simultaneous equations.

$$x + 3y = 11$$
$$3x + y = 9$$

$x + 3y = 11$ ($\times 3$)
$3x + y = 9$

$3x + 9y = 33$
$3x + y = 9$
‒ _____
$8y = 24$
$y = 3$

$x + 3y = 11$
$x + 9 = 11$
$x = 2$

$x = \underset{\checkmark}{..2..}$ $y = \underset{\checkmark}{..3..}$

[Total 3 marks]

2   Solve this pair of simultaneous equations.

$$2x + 3y = 12$$
$$5x + 4y = 9$$

$2x + 3y = 12$ ($\times 5$)
$5x + 4y = 9$ ($\times 2$)

$10x + 15y = 60$
$10x + 8y = 18$
‒ _____
$7y = 42$
$y = 6$

$2x + 3y = 12$ $y = 6$
$2x + 18 = 12$
$2x = {}^-6$
$x = {}^-3$

$x = \underset{\checkmark}{..{}^-3..}$ $y = \underset{\checkmark}{..6..}$

[Total 4 marks]

3   A sweet shop sells bags of pick 'n' mix. A bag that contains 4 chocolate frogs and 3 sugar mice costs £3.69. A bag that contains 6 chocolate frogs and 2 sugar mice costs £3.96.

How much would a bag that contains 2 chocolate frogs and 5 sugar mice cost?
Show your working.

$4f + 3m = 369$ ($\times 2$)
$6f + 2m = 396$ ($\times 3$)

$8f + 6m = 738$
$18f + 6m = 1188$
‒ _____
$10f = 450$
$f = 45$

1 chocolate frog $= £0.45$
1 sugar mouse $= £0.63$

$0.45 \times 2 = £0.90$
$0.63 \times 5 = £3.15$ } $=$

$4f + 3m = 369$ $f = 45$
$180 + 3m = 369$
-180
$3m = 189$
$m = 63$

£ $\underset{\checkmark}{..4.05..}$

[Total 4 marks]

Section Two — Algebra

$-2 + 2\sqrt{2}$

4 Solve the following pair of simultaneous equations.

$$x^2 + y = 4$$
$$y = 4x - 1$$

$x^2 + 4x - 1 = 4$
$\qquad\qquad -4$
$x^2 + 4x - 4 = 0$
$\qquad \swarrow \frac{1}{2}$
$(x + 2)^2 - 8$
$\qquad\qquad\qquad -8$
$(x + 2)(x + 2)$
$\qquad x^2 + 4x + 4$

$(x + 2)^2 - 8 = 0$
$(x + 2)^2 = 8$

$x = $ .... , $y = $ ....

and $x = $ .... , $y = $ ....

[Total 5 marks]

5 Solve the following pair of simultaneous equations.

$$2x^2 + y^2 = 51$$
$$y = x + 6$$

$x = $ .... , $y = $ ....

and $x = $ .... , $y = $ ....

[Total 5 marks]

6 The lines $y = x^2 + 3x - 1$ and $y = 2x + 5$ intersect at two points.
The line joining the two points has length $k\sqrt{5}$. Find the value of k.

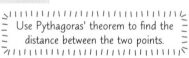
Use Pythagoras' theorem to find the distance between the two points.

$k = $ ....

[Total 6 marks]

Exam Practice Tip

When you're solving simultaneous equations in the exam, it's always a good idea to check your answers at the end. Just substitute your values for x and y back into the original equations and see if they add up as they should. If they don't then you must have gone wrong somewhere, so go back and check your working.

Score

27

Section Two — Algebra

Proof

1 Prove that $(3n + 2)^2 - (n + 2)^2 \equiv 8n(n + 1)$.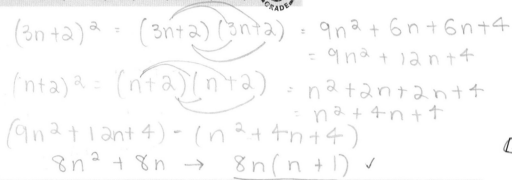

$(3n+2)^2 = (3n+2)(3n+2) = 9n^2 + 6n + 6n + 4$
$= 9n^2 + 12n + 4$

$(n+2)^2 = (n+2)(n+2) = n^2 + 2n + 2n + 4$
$= n^2 + 4n + 4$

$(9n^2 + 12n + 4) - (n^2 + 4n + 4)$
$8n^2 + 8n \rightarrow 8n(n+1)$ ✓

[Total 2 marks]

2 Jake says "If $a < b < c < d$ (where b and d are not zero), then $\frac{a}{b} < \frac{c}{d}$". Is he correct? Explain your answer.

[Total 3 marks]

3 Prove that the <u>difference</u> between the <u>squares</u> of two consecutive even numbers is always a <u>multiple of 4</u>.

[Total 3 marks]

4 Show that the number $2^{64} - 1$ is not prime.

[Total 3 marks]

Score:

11

Section Two — Algebra

Functions

1 f is a function such that $f(x) = \dfrac{3}{2x+5}$.

a) Find f(7.5) **(6)**

$f = \dfrac{3}{2(7.5)+5}$

$f = \dfrac{3}{20} =$

.........0.15.........
[1]

b) Find the inverse function f^{-1} in the form $f^{-1}(x)$. Show your working clearly. **(8)**

$f^{-1}(x) = $ ....
[3]

c) Show that $ff^{-1}(x) = x$. **(8)**

[3]

[Total 3 marks]

2 f and g are functions such that $f(x) = 2x^2 + 3$ and $g(x) = \sqrt{2x - 6}$.

a) Find g(21) **(6)**

$\sqrt{2(21) - 6}$

$\sqrt{42 - 6}$ $\sqrt{36} = 6$

.........6.........
[1]

b) Find gf(x) **(7)**

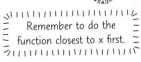
Remember to do the
function closest to x first.

$f = 2(6)^2 + 3$

$72 + 3$

75

gf(x) = ...75.........
[2]

c) Solve fg(a) = 7 **(7)**

a = ...
[3]

[Total 6 marks]

Score:

13

Straight Line Graphs

1   Line **L** passes through the points A (0, –3) and B (5, 7), as shown below.

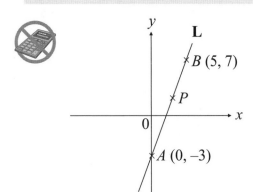

Diagram **NOT** to scale

x y x y
$(0, -3)$ $(5, 7)$

$$\frac{7 - -3}{5 - 0} = \frac{10}{5} = 2$$

$y = 2x - 3$

a) Find the equation of line **L**. **⑤**

.... $y = 2x - 3$ ....

[3]

b) Write down the equation of the line which is parallel to line **L** **⑤**
and passes through the point (2, 10).

$y = 2x + 10$

.... $y = 2x + 10$ ....

[2]

c) Point P lies on the line segment AB, such that $AP : PB = 2 : 3$ **⑦**
What are the coordinates of P?

....

[3]

[Total 8 marks]

2   The lines $y = 3x + 4$ and $y = 2x + 6$ intersect at the point M. **⑥**

Line **N** goes through point M and is parallel to the line $y = \frac{1}{2}x + 6$.

Find the equation of line **N**.

....

[Total 5 marks]

3 A straight line, **S**, passes through the points (a, b) and (c, d). **(7)**

It is given that: $2a + 4 = 2c$
$b - 6 = d$

[handwritten: $2a + 4 = 2c$ $b - 6 = d$]

a) What is the gradient of **S**?

Gradient = ...

[3]

b) Line **R** is perpendicular to Line **S** and passes through $(6, 3)$. Find the equation of the line.

....

[2]

[Total 5 marks]

4 James plots the points $A\,(5, 7)$, $B\,(1, -1)$, $C\,(13, 4)$ and $D\,(3, -2)$. He claims he can **(8)** draw a line perpendicular to AB that passes through the midpoint of both AB and CD.

Is he correct? Explain your answer.

[Total 4 marks]

Score: ☐

22

Quadratic Graphs

1 This graph below shows $y = x^2 - 3x + a$.

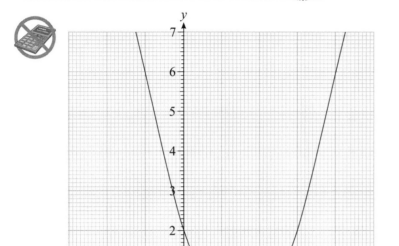

a) Estimate the coordinates of the turning point of $y = x^2 - 3x + a$

(........1.5...... , ...0.25......)

[1]

b) Write down the value of a.

$a = $ ....2..........

[1]

[Total 2 marks]

2 The temperature (T) of a piece of metal changes over time (t) as it is rapidly heated and then cooled again. It is modelled by the equation $T = -5t^2 + 40t - 35$.

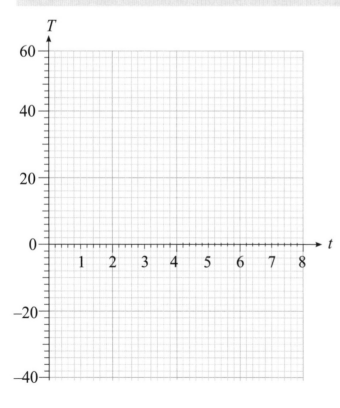

a) Plot the graph of $T = -5t^2 + 40t - 35$ on the grid.

[3]

b) At what time did the metal reach its highest temperature?

$t = $ ....

[1]

c) Using your graph, solve the equation $-5t^2 + 40t - 35 = 20$.

$t = $ .... and $t = $ ....

[2]

[Total 6 marks]

Section Three — Graphs

3 Sketch the graph of $y = 2x^2 + 10x - 12$. Label the turning point and any points where the curve intersects the axes with their coordinates. **(6)**

[Total 4 marks]

4 Find the turning point of $f(x) = x^2 + 4x + 6$. **(8)**

(.............. , ...)
[Total 4 marks]

Exam Practice Tip

If your curves aren't nice and smooth when you plot your quadratic graphs, you can be pretty sure you've gone wrong somewhere. Also keep an eye out for those sneaky turning point questions — complete the square if you can't find the exact turning point using your values or from the graph.

Score

16

Harder Graphs

1   Sketches of different graphs are shown below.

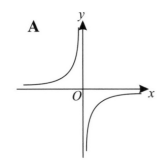 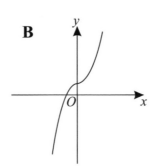 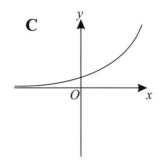

Match each equation below to one of the graphs above.

a) $x^3 + 1$ ....B..✓..

b) $y = \left(\frac{3}{2}\right)^x$ ....C......✓..

c) $y = -\frac{1}{x}$ ....A...✓..

[Total 3 marks]

2   This question is about the function $y = x^3 - 4x^2 + 4$.

a) Complete the table below.

x	-1	-0.5	0	0.5	1	1.5	2	2.5	3	3.5	4
y	-1	2.875	4	3.125	1	-1.625	-4				

[2]

b) Use your table to draw the graph of $y = x^3 - 4x^2 + 4$ on the grid, for values of x in the range $-1 \leq x \leq 4$.

[2]

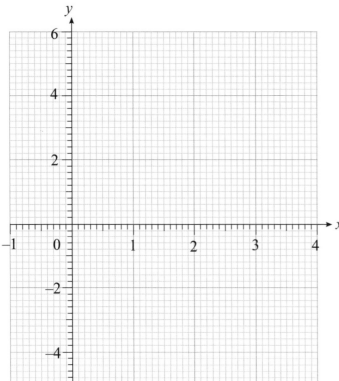

c) Estimate the solutions of the equation $x^3 - 4x^2 + 4 = 0$.

....

[1]

[Total 5 marks]

Don't use a ruler to join up the dots in curved graphs.

3 Sketch the following trigonometric graphs, labelling the points where the graphs cross the *x*- and *y*-axes and any points where the graph is undefined. $\underset{\text{GRADE}}{\overset{\text{GRADE}}{\textbf{7}}}$

a) $\cos x$ for $0° \leq x \leq 360°$

[2]

b) $\tan x$ for $-180° \leq x \leq 180°$

[3]

[Total 5 marks]

4 A curve has the equation $x^2 + y^2 = 16$. $\underset{\text{GRADE}}{\overset{\text{GRADE}}{\textbf{7}}}$

a) Does this curve pass through the origin?
Explain your answer.

....

....

....

[2]

b) Find the values of *x* for which the curve intersects the *x*-axis.

....

[1]

[Total 3 marks]

Exam Practice Tip

There are loads of different types of graphs to learn — it's really just a matter of practising recognising them from their equations until they're all firmly lodged in your noggin. If you're really stuck in the exam, try sticking different values of x into the equation and making a rough plot of the graph to spark your memory.

Score

16

Section Three — Graphs

Solving Equations Using Graphs

1   The graphs of the equations $y = \dfrac{6}{x-2}$ and $y = 2x - 5$ are shown below.

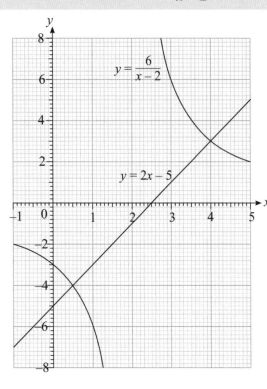

Using the graphs, write down the solutions to the simultaneous equations

$y = \dfrac{6}{x-2}$ and $y = 2x - 5$.

$x = $ .... , $y = $ ....

$x = $ .... , $y = $ ....

[Total 2 marks]

2   The graph of the curve $y = x^2 + 2x - 5$ is shown below.
By drawing a suitable line on the graph, find the solutions of $x^2 + x = 6$

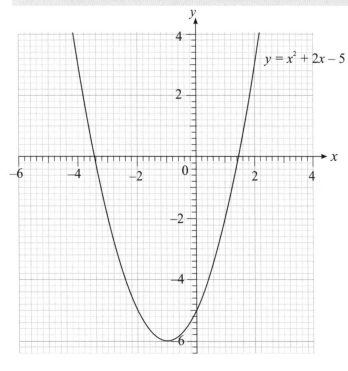

$x = $ ....

$x = $ ....

[Total 4 marks]

Score:

6

Graph Transformations

1 The diagram below shows a sketch of the graph $y = f(x)$.

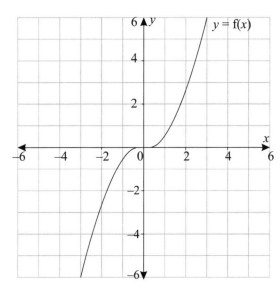

a) On the same axes sketch the graph of $y = f(x - 2)$.

[2]

b) Give the coordinates of the point where your curve crosses the x-axis.

(................. , ...)

[1]

[Total 3 marks]

2 The diagram below shows the graph of $f(x)$ for $f(x) = x^2 + 3x + 2$.

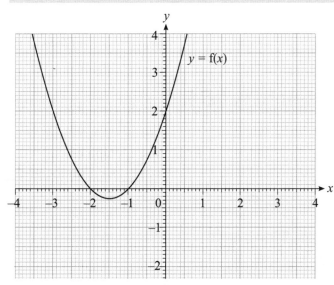

a) Determine whether $y = f(x + 1) - 2$ has any real roots. If so, write down their coordinates.

....

....

....

....

[2]

b) Estimate the minimum point of the graph of $y = f(x - 4) + 1$.

(................. , ...)

[3]

[Total 5 marks]

46

3 The graph of $y = \sin x$ for $0° \leq x \leq 360°$ is shown on the grids below.

a) On this grid draw the graph of $y = \sin(x - 45)°$

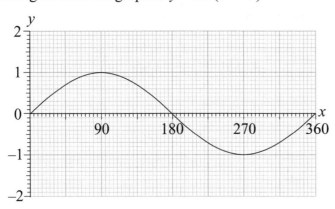

[1]

b) On this grid draw the graph of $y = -\sin x$

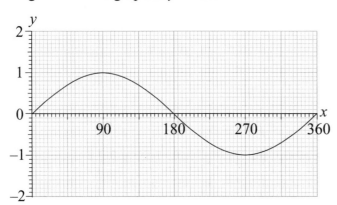

[1]

[Total 2 marks]

4 The graph of $y = \cos x$ for $0° \leq x \leq 360°$ is shown below.

a) Draw the graph of
$y = \cos(-x) + 1$ on the grid.

[2]

b) Write down the x-values of the points where $y = -\cos(x + 30)$ crosses the x-axis.

....

[2]

[Total 4 marks]

Score:

14

Section Three — Graphs

Real-Life Graphs

1 An electricity company offers its customers two different price plans.

Plan **A**:
Monthly tariff of £18, plus 10p for each unit used.

Plan **B**:
No monthly tariff, just pay 40p for each unit used.

a) Use the graph to find the cost of using
70 units in a month for each plan.

Plan **A** ...25..... Plan **B** ...28.....

[2]

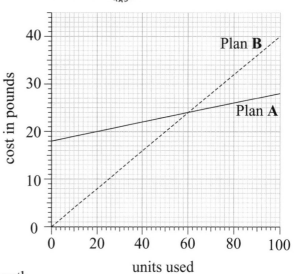

b) Mr Barker uses about 85 units of electricity each month.
Which price plan would you advise him to choose? Explain your answer.

...Plan A, because it is cheaper than plan B.......

......

[2]

[Total 4 marks]

2 Each of the vessels below is filled with water at a constant rate.

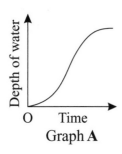 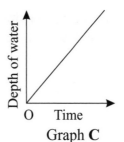 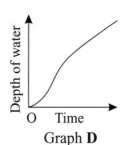

   1   2   3   4

Each of these graphs show the depth of water within a vessel in relation to time.

   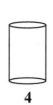

Graph **A**   Graph **B**   Graph **C**   Graph **D**

Match the vessel with the correct graph.

Graph **A** and ..2.... Graph **B** and ..3.. Graph **C** and ..4.. Graph **D** and ..1....

[Total 2 marks]

Score:

6

Distance-Time Graphs

1 The distance-time graph below shows a 30 km running race between Selby and Tyrone.

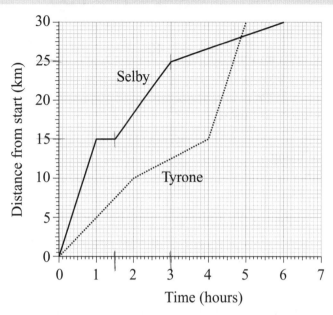

a) During the race Selby stops at a bench to get his breath back.
   After how many hours did he stop at the bench?

   ....1....... hours
   [1]

b) Who won the race? How can you tell this from the graph?

   Tyrone, because he finished the 30km in 5 hours
   whereas Selby finished in 6 hours.
   [1]

c) What was Selby's speed between 1.5 and 3 hours into the race? Give your answer to 2 d.p.

   $S = \dfrac{d}{t}$ $S = \dfrac{10\,km}{1.5\,hours}$

   $s = km/h$

   $\dfrac{10}{1.5} = 6.\dot{6}$ $6.66|666$ 6.67

   ....6.67....... km/h
   [2]

d) During the race, one of the runners injured their leg.
   Which runner do you think was injured?
   What evidence is there on the graph to support your answer?

   Selby was injured as he stopped for 30 minutes
   after being 1 hour into the race. After stopping
   he continues with the race gradually and slower
   than he was running before, this is evidence   *[2]*
   that Selby slowed down due to his   *[Total 6 marks]*
   injured leg.

   Score:

   6

Velocity-Time Graphs

1 The velocity of a motorcycle is recorded over a minute.

a) Draw a velocity-time graph using the following information:
The motorcycle sets off from a standstill, accelerating at a constant rate for 10 seconds until it is moving at 10 m/s. It moves at a constant speed for the next 20 seconds.
The motorcycle then accelerates at a constant rate for 7 seconds until it is moving at 24 m/s.
It moves at the same speed for 15 seconds before decelerating until it stops after 8 seconds.

[3]

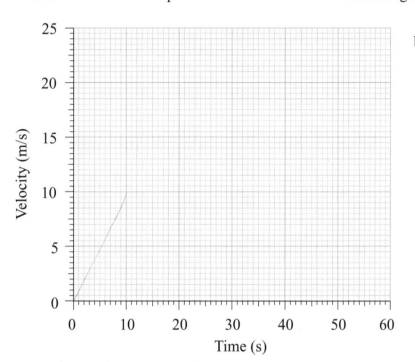

b) Calculate the acceleration of the motorcycle at 35 seconds.

.... m/s²
[1]
[Total 4 marks]

2 James rolls a ball down a hill and records its velocity.
He plots the results on the velocity-time graph shown below.

Remember, the area under the graph = total distance travelled.

Calculate the average speed of the ball.
Give your answer to 1 s.f.

.... m/s
[Total 4 marks]

Score:

8

Gradients of Curves

1 The graph of $y = x^3 - 2x$ is shown below.

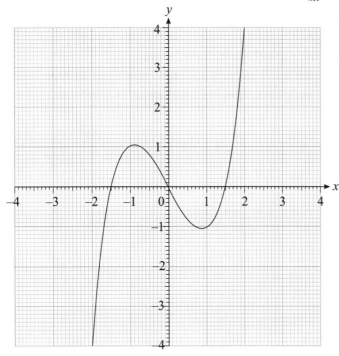

a) Estimate the gradient of the graph at $x = -1$

....

[2]

b) Find the average gradient of the graph between $x = -1$ and $x = 1$

....

[2]

[Total 4 marks]

2 The graph below shows how the velocity of a moving vehicle changes over time.

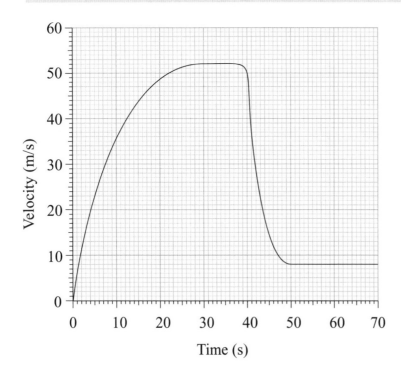

a) Find the average acceleration of the vehicle between 5 seconds and 25 seconds.

.... m/s²

[2]

b) Estimate the acceleration of the vehicle at 45 seconds.

.... m/s²

[2]

[Total 4 marks]

Score:

8

Ratios

1   Eve is making a bird house. To make the walls, she takes a piece of wood and cuts it into four pieces in the ratio $5:6:6:7$. The longest wall is 9 cm longer than the shortest wall.

    How long was the original piece of wood?

.... cm

[Total 3 marks]

2   Hannah is making some green paint to paint her kitchen wall.
She makes it by mixing together $3\frac{3}{4}$ tins of yellow paint and $1\frac{1}{2}$ tins of blue paint.
The tins are all the same size.

a) Express this ratio in its simplest form.

....

[2]

b) How much of each paint will Hannah need to make 2800 ml of green paint?

yellow paint .... ml

blue paint .... ml

[2]

[Total 4 marks]

3   Edmund, Susan and Peter shared £150 in the ratio $(4x + 10):(2x + 5):(5x + 3)$.

    How much money did each person get?

$4x + 10 + 2x + 5 + 5x + 3$

$11x + 18 = £150$
$\quad -18$
$11x = 132$
$x = 12$

$4x + 10 \quad x = 12$ $2x + 5 \quad x = 12$ $5x + 3 \quad x = 12$
$48 + 10$ $24 + 5$ $60 + 3$
$£58$ $£29$ 63

Edmund: £ ..58..............

Susan: £ ..29..............

Peter: £ ..63..............

[Total 4 marks]

4   Chocolate milkshake is made by mixing milk and ice cream in the ratio 2 : 9.

a) Give the amount of milk used as a fraction of the ice cream used.

2 + 9 : 11 $\frac{2}{11}$

.........$\frac{2}{11}$.........

[1]

b) How much milkshake is made if 801 ml of ice cream are used?

2 : 9

801 ml

89 × 2 : 178

.........178......... ml

[2]

c) On the axes below, draw a graph that can be used to work out
the amount of ice cream needed, given the amount of milk used.

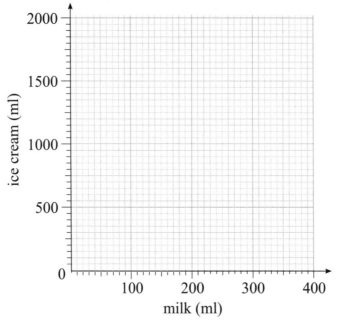

[2]

[Total 5 marks]

5   Mr Appleseed's Supercompost is made by mixing soil, compost and grit in the ratio 4 : 3 : 1.
Soil costs £8 per 40 kg, compost costs £15 per 25 kg and grit costs £12 per 15 kg.

How much profit will be made if 16 kg of Mr Appleseed's Supercompost is sold for £10?

£ ....

[Total 5 marks]

Section Four — Ratio, Proportion and Rates of Change

6 In the morning a baker makes x muffins and y pastries.
After selling 5 muffins and 3 pastries, the ratio of muffins to pastries is $5:8$.
He then makes 10 more of each item and the ratio becomes $5:7$.

Find the values of x and y.

$x -$ .... $: y -$ .... $= 5:8$ and $x +$ .... $: y +$ .... $= 5:7$

$$\frac{\text{........} - \text{........}}{\text{........} - \text{........}} = \frac{5}{8} \quad \text{and} \quad \frac{\text{........} + \text{........}}{\text{........} + \text{........}} = \frac{5}{7}$$

$8(\text{......} - \text{......}) = 5(\text{......} - \text{......})$ and $7(\text{......} + \text{......}) = 5(\text{......} + \text{......})$

Expand and simplify to give ......$x -$ ......$y = 25$ [1] and ......$x -$ ......$y = 0$ [2]

[1] $-$ [2]: $x =$ ....

Substitute $x =$ .... into [1]: (...... $\times$ ......) $-$ ......$y = 25$

...... $y =$ .... , so $y =$ ....

$x =$ ....

$y =$ ....

[Total 5 marks]

7 Fabio has a large jar containing only black and green olives.
The probability of randomly choosing a black olive from the jar is $\frac{5}{16}$.
After eating 1 green and 3 black olives the probability of choosing a black olive is $\frac{3}{10}$.

How many black and green olives were originally in the jar?

Start by finding the ratios of black to green olives before and after he eats some — careful though, the original ratio of black:green isn't 5:16.

Black olives: ....

Green olives: ....

[Total 6 marks]

Exam Practice Tip

Ratio questions that include a changing ratio can be tough — you'll often need to set up a pair of equations and solve them simultaneously. Luckily you can always use the same method to do this. Write the ratios as equations, turn the ratios into fractions, multiply out the fractions and solve the equations simultaneously.

Score

32

Direct and Inverse Proportion

1   Ishmael is making some t-shirts. It takes 5 m² of cotton to make 8 t-shirts. (GRADE 4)
2 m² of cotton costs £5.50.

How much will it cost Ishmael to buy enough cotton to make 85 t-shirts?

£ ....

[Total 4 marks]

2   Neil and Sophie are harvesting some crops. Sophie needs to harvest (GRADE 4)
three times as many crops as Neil but she can harvest them twice as quick.

Neil takes 3.5 hours to harvest his crops. How long does Sophie take to harvest her crops?

.... hours

[Total 3 marks]

3   Elijah runs a go-kart track. It takes 12 litres of petrol to (GRADE 4)
race 8 go-karts for 20 minutes. Petrol costs £1.37 per litre.

a) 6 go-karts used 18 litres of petrol. How many minutes did they race for?

.... minutes

[4]

b) How much does the petrol cost to run 8 go-karts for 45 minutes?

£ ....

[3]

[Total 7 marks]

4 Sketch the following proportions on the axes below them.

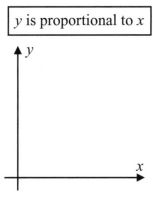

y is proportional to x

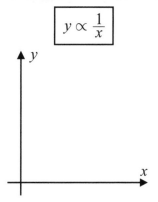

$y \propto \dfrac{1}{x}$

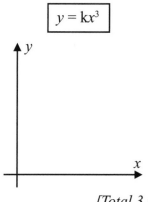

$y = kx^3$

[Total 3 marks]

5 The gravitational force, f, between two objects is inversely proportional to the square of the distance, d, between them. When $d = 100$, $f = 20$.

Write an equation connecting f and d and use it to find the value of f when $d = 800$.

$f = $ ....

[Total 3 marks]

6 Round a bend on a railway track the height difference (h mm) between the outer and inner rails must vary in direct proportion to the square of the maximum permitted speed (S km/h).

a) When $S = 50$, $h = 35$. Calculate h when $S = 40$. (7)

$h = $ ....
[3]

b) The maximum speed on a bend is to be increased by 30%. What will be the percentage increase in the height difference between the outer and inner rails?

.... %
[4]
[Total 7 marks]

Score:

27

Percentages

1 A computer costs £927 plus VAT, where VAT is charged at 20%. Find the total cost of the computer.

$£927$
$10\% = £92.70$
$20\% = £92.70 \times 2$
$\quad\quad = £185.40$
$£927 + £185.40 = £1112.40$

    92.70   927
    × ? 2   + 185.40
   185.40   1112.40

£ ...1112.40✓

[Total 3 marks]

2 The ratio of grapes to cherries in a fruit salad is 2 : 5. Circle the correct statement below.

There are 50% more cherries than grapes.   There are 80% more cherries than grapes.

There are 20% as many grapes as cherries.   There are 40% as many grapes as cherries.

[Total 1 mark]

3 After an 8% pay rise Mr Brown's salary was £15 714.

What was his salary before the increase?

$15714 \times 8\% = 121.12$
$15714 - 121.12 = 15592.88$

£ ...15592.88

[Total 3 marks]

4 Jane has an annual salary of £45 000 before tax.

She pays no tax on the first £10 000 of her income — this is her tax-free allowance.
She pays tax at 20% on any income between £10 000 and £41 865,
and at 40% on any income over £41 865.

What percentage of her £45 000 annual salary does Jane pay in tax?
Give your answer to 1 decimal place.

.... %

[Total 4 marks]

Section Four — Ratio, Proportion and Rates of Change

5   In a pet rescue shelter, 50% of the animals are cats and 40% of the cats are black. **(4)**

a) What percentage of the animals at the shelter are black cats?

.... %

[2]

b) There are 90 animals at the shelter, how many are not black cats?

....

[2]

[Total 4 marks]

6   Ian makes and sells lobster pots. He sells them for £32 per pot which is a 60% profit **(5)** on the cost of the materials. He wants to increase his profit to 88%.

How much should Ian start charging per lobster pot?

£ ....

[Total 3 marks]

7   Sophie and two friends are booking festival tickets online using their credit cards. **(5)** Tickets cost £180 each, plus an additional charge of £5.40 per credit card transaction.

a) What is the percentage increase in the cost of buying one ticket if it's bought using a credit card?

.... %

[2]

b) What is the percentage saving if Sophie and her friends buy three tickets in one transaction rather than three separate transactions? Give your answer to 2 d.p.

.... %

[3]

[Total 5 marks]

8 A hairdresser recorded some details about her customers one day.
The ratio of children : adults was 3 : 7.
60% of the children had blond hair and 20% of the adults had blond hair.

What percentage of all the customers had blond hair?

.... %

[Total 4 marks]

9 In the triangular prism below, the base and vertical height of
the triangular face are x cm and the length of the prism is y cm.

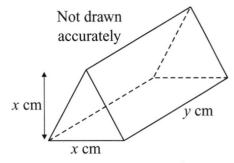

Not drawn
accurately

x cm

y cm

x cm

a) Work out the percentage increase in the area of the
triangular face when x is increased by 15%.

.... %

[4]

b) Calculate the percentage decrease in y that is required to keep the volume of
the prism unchanged when x is increased by 15%. Give your answer to 1 d.p.

.... %

[5]

[Total 9 marks]

Compound Growth and Decay

1   Mrs Burdock borrows £750 to buy a sofa.
    She is charged 6% interest per annum.

    ⌇⁣‖‖‖‖‖‖‖‖‖‖‖‖‖‖‖‖‖‖⌇
    ⌇ Per annum just means per year. ⌇
    ⌇‖‖‖‖‖‖‖‖‖‖‖‖‖‖‖‖‖‖⌇

    If Mrs Burdock doesn't pay back any of the money for 3 years, how much will she owe?
    Give your answer to the nearest penny.

    Multiplier = 1 + ... = ...

    In 3 years she will owe: £750 × (.............)⁻ = £ ....

                                                    £ ....
                                                    [Total 2 marks]

2   The population of fish in a lake is estimated to decrease by 8% every year.

    a) How many fish will be left after 15 years if the initial population is 2000?

    ⌇‖‖‖‖‖‖‖‖‖‖‖‖‖‖‖‖‖‖⌇
    ⌇ TIP: think about which way you ⌇   ....
    ⌇ should round your answer. ⌇   *[2]*
    ⌇‖‖‖‖‖‖‖‖‖‖‖‖‖‖‖‖‖‖⌇

    b) How many years will it take for the population of fish to be less than $\frac{3}{4}$ of the initial population?

    $\frac{3}{4}$ of the initial population = ...

    2000 × .... = ...

    .... × ....^{2} = ...

    .... × ....^{3} = ...

    .... × ....^{4} = ...

                                                    .... years
                                                    [2]

                                                    [Total 4 marks]

3   A conservation company plants pine trees in a forest to increase their number
    by 16% each year. At the end of each year, a logging company is permitted
    to cut down up to 75% of the number of new trees planted that year.

    At the start of 2013 there were 5000 pine trees in the forest.
    What was the minimum number of pine trees in the forest at the end of 2014?

                                                    ....
                                                    [Total 4 marks]

4 Rich inherits £10 000, and wants to invest it. His bank is offering him two accounts.

Compound Collectors Account	*Simple Savers Account*
5.5% compound interest per year, paid annually into your account.	*6.2% simple interest paid annually by cheque.*
Rate is guaranteed for 5 years.	*Rate guaranteed for 5 years, no further deposits permitted after opening.*

a) After 5 years, which account will give him the largest balance?

....

[4]

b) Why might Rich not want to invest in the Simple Savers Account?

....

....

[1]

[Total 5 marks]

5 Mrs Khan puts £2500 into a high interest savings account. Interest is added to the account at the end of each year. After 2 years Mrs Khan's account contains £2704.

What is the interest rate on Mrs Khan's account?

.... %

[Total 3 marks]

6 The value of a football player decreases at a rate of 25% each year after the age of 30. At the age of 35 a player was valued at £2 000 000.

What was the player's value when he was 31 years old? Give your answer to the nearest £100 000.

£ ....

[Total 3 marks]

Score:

21

Section Four — Ratio, Proportion and Rates of Change

Speed

1   John and Alan hired a van. Their receipt gave them information about how much time they spent travelling in the van, and how fast they went. **(3)**

$s = \dfrac{d}{t}$

> Travelling time: 1 hour 15 minutes
> Average speed: 56 km/h

Calculate the distance that John and Alan travelled in the van.

$d = s \times t$
$d = 56 \times 1.25$
$d = 70$

.................70................. km
[Total 2 marks]

2   Adam has been caught speeding by a pair of average speed cameras. The speed limit was <u>50 mph</u>. **(4)**

The cameras are 2500 m apart. The time taken for his car to pass between them was 102 seconds.

a) What was Adam's average speed between the cameras?
    Give your answer to the nearest mph. Take 1 mile as 1.6 km.

.... mph
[3]

b) If Adam had been travelling within the speed limit, what is the minimum time it should have taken him to pass between the cameras? Give your answer to the nearest second.

.... s
[2]

[Total 5 marks]

3   In 2013 Mo ran a long-distance race and finished with time *t*. In 2014 he finished the same race but his time was 10% quicker. **(6)**

> Hint: the distance will be the same for both races.

By what percentage did his average speed for the race increase?
Give your answer to 2 decimal places.

.... %
[Total 4 marks]

Score: ☐

11

       Section Four — Ratio, Proportion and Rates of Change

Density

1 The mass of a metal statue is 360 kg.
The density of the metal alloy from which it is made is 1800 kg/m³. **(3)**

a) Calculate the volume of the statue.

$d = \frac{m}{v}$ $v = \frac{m}{d}$ $v = \frac{360}{1800} = 0.2$

........................0.2........................ m³
[2]

b) It is decided that the metal statue is too heavy so a different metal alloy is used to make
a new statue. The new statue has the same volume as the old one but has a mass of 220 kg.
Calculate the density of the new statue.

$D = \frac{m}{v}$

$d = \frac{220}{0.2}$

........................1100........................ kg/m³
[2]

[Total 4 marks]

2 An iron cube has side length 4 cm and iron has a density of 7.9 grams per cm³. **(4)**

a) Work out the mass of the iron cube. $d = 7.9\ g/cm^3$

$d = \frac{m}{v}$

$4cm$ $4 \times 4 \times 4 = 64\ cm^3$ $m = d \times v$
$m = 7.9 \times 64 = 505.6$

........................505.6........................ g
[3]

b) A larger iron cube has a mass of 63.2 kg.
What is the ratio of the side lengths of the smaller and larger cubes?

....

[4]

[Total 7 marks]

3 Brass is a metallic alloy. One type of brass consists only of copper and zinc in the ratio **(6)**
7 : 3 by volume. Copper has a density of 8.9 g/cm³ and zinc has a density of 7.1 g/cm³.

What is the density of this type of brass?

.... g/cm³

[Total 4 marks]

Score: ☐

15

☹ ☐   ☺ ☐   ☺ ☐

Pressure

1   The cuboid below has three different faces (A, B and C).  The cuboid has a weight of 40 N.

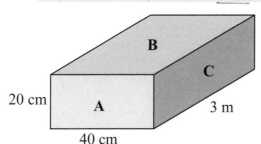

20 cm

A

40 cm

3 m

a) Calculate the pressure, in N/m^2, that the cuboid exerts on horizontal ground when the cuboid is resting on face A.

.... N/m^2

[3]

b) Three of these cuboids are stacked directly on top of each other and the bottom cuboid is resting on face B. What pressure are they exerting on horizontal ground?

.... N/m^2

[3]

[Total 6 marks]

2   The cone below has a base diameter of 20x cm. When the base of 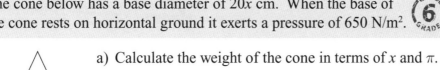 the cone rests on horizontal ground it exerts a pressure of 650 N/m^2.

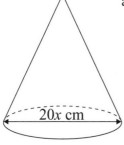

20x cm

a) Calculate the weight of the cone in terms of x and π.

.... N

[4]

b) The diameter of the cone is halved but the weight is kept the same. What effect will this have on the pressure exerted on the ground?

[2]

[Total 6 marks]

Exam Practice Tip

You might think remembering the formulas for speed, density and pressure is tough but questions involving speed, density or pressure often involve some conversion of units too. Make sure you're happy converting: metric/imperial units, speeds, areas and volumes so you don't make any silly mistakes when exam time comes.

Score

12

Geometry

1   A triangle is shown in the diagram below.

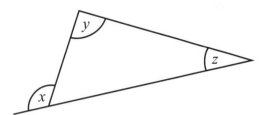

Prove that $x = y + z$.

[Total 3 marks]

2   *DEF* and *BEC* are straight lines that cross at *E*.
AFB and *AC* are perpendicular lines.

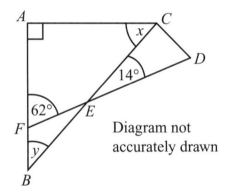

a) Find angle *x*.
   Give a reason for each stage of your working.

Diagram not accurately drawn

$x =$ ....$^{\circ}$

[2]

b) Hence show that $y = 48°$.

[2]

[Total 4 marks]

3   The diagram shows a parallelogram.

Prove that $x = y$.

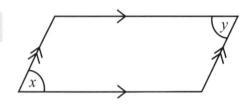

[Total 3 marks]

4   *AB* and *CD* are parallel lines. *EF* and *GH* are straight lines.

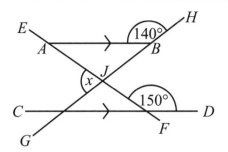

Work out the size of angle *x*.
Give reasons for each stage of your working.

Diagram not accurately drawn

....°

[Total 4 marks]

5   Lines *AB* and *DE* are parallel and *ABC* is a straight line.
Lines *AE*, *BC* and *BD* are of equal length.

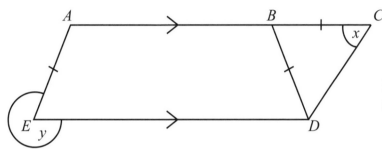

Diagram not
accurately drawn

Find an expression for *y* in terms of *x*.

....

[Total 5 marks]

6   *ABCD* is a trapezium. Lines *AB* and *DC* are parallel to each other.

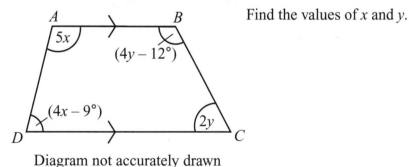

Find the values of *x* and *y*.

Diagram not accurately drawn

x = ...° *y* = ...°

[Total 4 marks]

Exam Practice Tip

If you find yourself staring at a geometry problem in the exam not knowing where to start, just try finding any angles you can — don't worry tooooo much at first about the particular angle you've been asked to find. Go through the rules of geometry one at a time, and apply them wherever you can.

Score

23

                Section Five — Geometry and Measures

Polygons

1 One of the angles in a rhombus is 62°.

What are the sizes of its other three angles?

$62° \times 2 = 124°$

$\begin{array}{r} 3\cancel{6}0° \\ -124° \\ \hline 236 \end{array}$

$\begin{array}{r} 118 \\ 2\overline{)236°} \end{array}$

.......62 ✓°, ...118 ✓° and ....118 ✓°

[Total 2 marks]

2 *ABCD* is a kite. Line *DX* is the same length as line *AD*.

Find the size of angle *DAB*.

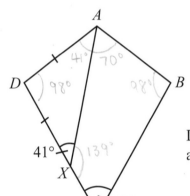

Diagram not
accurately drawn

$180 - (41 \times 2) =$

$180 - 82 = 98$

$180 - 41 = 139$

$139 + 53 + 98 =$

$\begin{array}{r} 139 \\ + 53 \\ \hline 192 \\ + 98 \\ \hline 290 \end{array}$

$360 - 290 = 70$

$70 + 41 = 111°$

.......111 ✓°

[Total 3 marks]

3 Part of a regular polygon is shown below. Each interior angle is 150°.

Diagram not
accurately drawn

 Calculate the number of sides of the polygon.

$360 \div 30 = 12$

.......12 ✓

[Total 3 marks]

Section Five — Geometry and Measures

4 The diagram shows a regular octagon. *AB* is a side of the octagon and *O* is its centre.

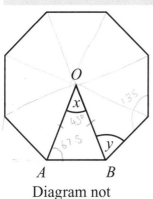

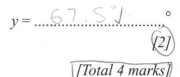

a) Work out the size of the angle marked *x*.

$360 \div 8 = 45°$

x = ...45°...✓........ °

[2]

b) Work out the size of the angle marked *y*.

$180 - 45 = 135$

180

y = ...67.5✓... °

[2]

[Total 4 marks]

5 Shape *ABCDEF* is an irregular hexagon.

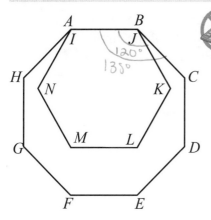

Prove that the sum of the interior angles of the shape is 720°.
Show all your working.

Angles of triangle add to 180°

$720° \div 4 = 180°$ ✓

[Total 3 marks]

6 The diagram below shows a regular hexagon inside a regular octagon.
Vertices *A* and *B* coincide with vertices *I* and *J* respectively.

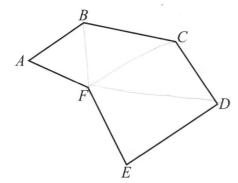

Find the size of angle *CBK*.

Hexagon
$(6 - 2) \times 180 = 720 \div 6 = 120$

Octagon
$(8 - 2) \times 180 = 1080 \div 8 = 135$

$135 - 120 = 15$

...15✓... °

[Total 2 marks]

Exam Practice Tip

You need to know the number of sides of a regular polygon to work out its interior and exterior angles —
so make sure you've swotted up on the different types of polygon. Altogether now: equilateral triangle (3),
square (4), pentagon (5), hexagon (6), heptagon (7), octagon (8), nonagon (9), decagon (10).

Score

17

17

   ✓

Circle Geometry

1   The diagram below shows a circle with centre *O*. *A*, *B*, *C* and *D* are points on the circumference of the circle and *AOC* is a straight line.

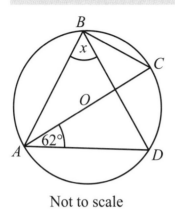

Not to scale

  Work out the size of the angle marked *x*.

x = ...°

[Total 3 marks]

2   The diagram shows a circle with centre *O*. *A*, *B* and *C* are points on the circumference. *AD* and *CD* are tangents to the circle and *ABE* is a straight line. Angle *CDO* is 24°.

Find the size of angle *CBE*.

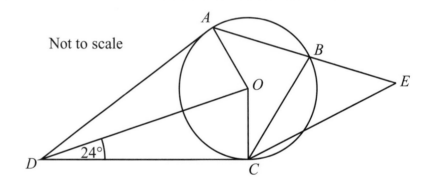

Not to scale

............................°

[Total 5 marks]

3   In the diagram below, *A*, *B*, *C* and *D* are points on the circumference of the circle. *EDB* is a straight line and *FG* is the tangent to the circle at point *B*. Angle *FBD* is 102° and angle *EDC* is 147°.

Find the size of angle *CAD*. Give reasons for each step of your answer.

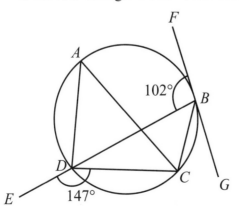

............................°

[Total 4 marks]

4 In the diagram, *O* is the centre of the circle. *A*, *B*, *C* and *D* are points on the circumference of the circle and *DE* and *BE* are tangents. Angle *DEB* is 80°.

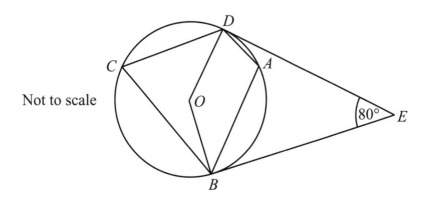

Not to scale

 Work out the size of angle *DAB*, giving reasons for each step in your working.

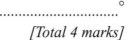

[Total 4 marks]

5 Points *A*, *B*, *C*, *D* and *E* lie on the circumference of the circle shown in the diagram below. Angle *ABE* is 37° and angle *DCE* is 53°. *FG* is the tangent to the circle at point *E*.

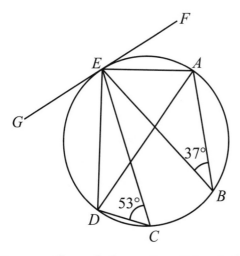

Not to scale

Prove that the chord *AD* passes through the centre of the circle.

[Total 3 marks]

Section Five — Geometry and Measures

70

70

6 *A, B, C* and *D* are points on the circumference of the circle with centre *O*.
FE is the tangent to the circle at *D* and angle *BDE* = 53°.

a) Find the size of angle *DOB*.

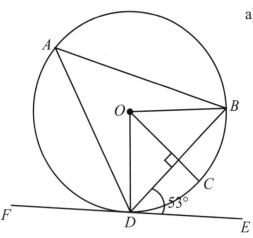

Diagram not accurately drawn

.............................°

[2]

b) Explain why angle *COB* is half the size of angle *DOB*

....

....

....

[2]

[Total 4 marks]

7 *A, B, C* and *D* are points on the circumference of the circle shown below.

Show that *X* is not the centre of the circle.

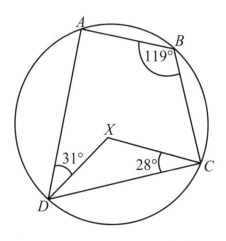

Diagram not accurately drawn

[Total 3 marks]

Exam Practice Tip

Make sure you know the rules about circles really, really well. Draw them out and stick them all over your bedroom walls, your fridge, even your dog. Then in the exam, go through the rules one-by-one and use them to fill in as many angles in the diagram as you can. Keep an eye out for sneaky isosceles triangles too.

Score

26

Congruent Shapes

1   *ABC* is a triangle. *FDEC* is a parallelogram such that *F* is the midpoint of *AC*,
     D is the midpoint of *AB* and *E* is the midpoint of *BC*.

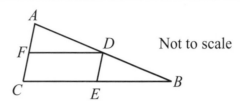

A
D   Not to scale
F
C   *E*   *B*

Prove that triangles *AFD* and *DEB* are congruent.

F is the midpoint of AC so AF = ..., and opposite sides of a parallelogram are
equal so .... = FC. Therefore AF = ...

E is the midpoint of CB so .... = EB, and opposite sides of a parallelogram are
equal so .... = FD. Therefore FD = ...

D is the midpoint of AB, so AD = ...

Satisfies condition .... so triangles are congruent.   *[Total 4 marks]*

2   The diagram shows two overlapping circles, with centres *O* and *P*.
     The circles intersect at *M* and *N*, and the centre of each circle is a point on the
     circumference of the other circle. *KOPL* is a straight line. *KM* and *NL* are parallel to each other.

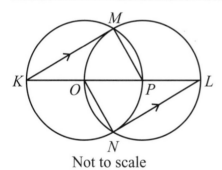

Prove that triangles *KMP* and *LNO* are congruent.

M
K   *O*   *P*   *L*
N
Not to scale   [Total 4 marks]

3   *A*, *B*, *C* and *D* are points on a circle. *AED* and *BEC* are straight lines.
     AC and *BD* are the same length as each other.

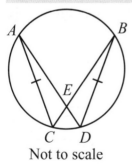

Prove that triangles *AEC* and *BED* are congruent.

A   *B*
E
C   *D*
Not to scale   [Total 3 marks]

Exam Practice Tip

To prove two triangles are congruent, you need to show that three pairs of angles or sides are the same.
Give a reason for each step of working — to get all the marks you need to explain <u>why</u> things are equal.
Then give the condition for congruence that you've satisfied (SSS, AAS, SAS or RHS).

Score

11

Similar Shapes

1 The shapes *ABCD* and *EFGH* are mathematically similar.

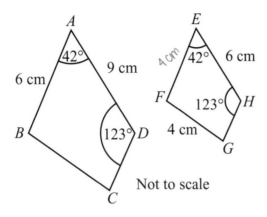

Not to scale

a) Find the length of *EF*.

.........4......... cm

[2]

b) Find the length of *BC*.

.......6........ cm

[1]

[Total 3 marks]

2 James wants to estimate the height of a flagpole in his local park. He finds that if he stands a horizontal distance of 63 m away from the flagpole and holds his index finger up in front of him it exactly covers the flagpole.

James' finger is 8 cm long and he holds it at a horizontal distance of 60 cm away from his body. Use this information to find an estimate for the height of the flagpole.

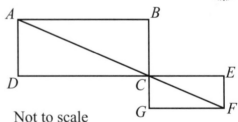

Not to scale

.... m

[Total 3 marks]

3 *ABCD* and *CEFG* are rectangles that touch at *C*. *DCE*, *BCG* and *ACF* are straight lines.

Prove that triangles *ABC* and *CEF* are similar triangles.

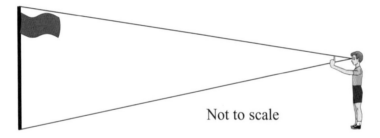

Not to scale

[Total 3 marks]

Score:

9

The Four Transformations

1 Shapes **F** and **G** have been drawn on the grid below.

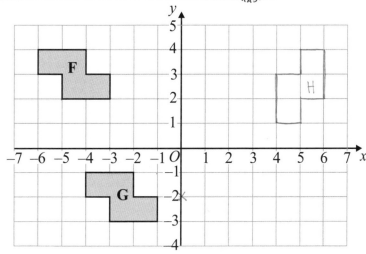

 a) Write down the vector which describes the translation that maps **F** onto **G**.

$$\begin{pmatrix} 2 \\ -5 \end{pmatrix}$$ ✓

....

[2]

b) Rotate shape **F** by 90° clockwise around the point (0, −2).
   Label your image **H**.

✓

[2]

[Total 4 marks]

2 In the diagram below, **B** is an image of **A**. ③

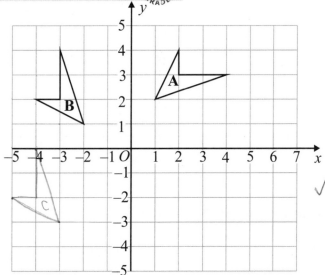

a) Describe fully the single transformation that maps **A** onto **B**.

.... Shape A is rotated 90° ∨ anticlockwise from point (0, 0) to ....✓....
.... get Shape B ....

[3]

b) Translate shape **B** by the vector $\begin{pmatrix} -1 \\ -4 \end{pmatrix}$.
   Label the image as **C**.

[1]

[Total 4 marks]

Section Five — Geometry and Measures

74

3 Triangle **R** has been drawn on the grid below.

 Reflect triangle **R** in the line $y = x$ and then enlarge it with centre $(6, -3)$ and scale factor 3. Label the resulting shape **S**.

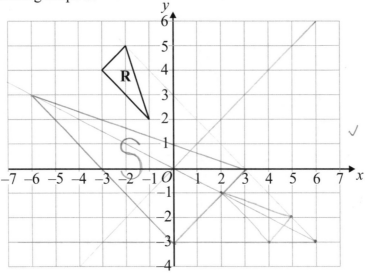

[Total 3 marks]

4 Triangle **A** has been drawn on the grid below.

 Enlarge triangle **A** by scale factor $\frac{1}{2}$ with centre of enlargement $(-6, 1)$. Label your image **B**.

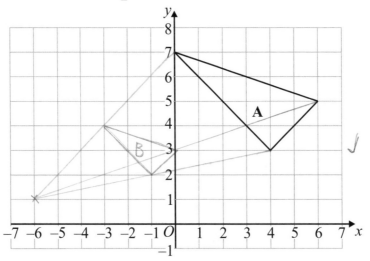

[Total 2 marks]

5 A triangle has been drawn on the grid below.

 Enlarge the triangle by a scale factor of -2 about the point **C**.

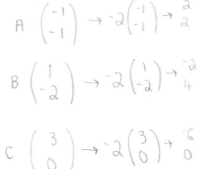

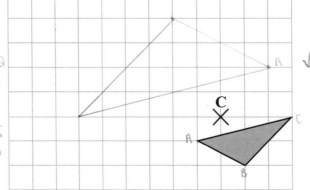

[Total 2 marks]

Score:

15

Section Five — Geometry and Measures

Perimeter and Area

1 Lynn is designing a garden. The diagram shows her design.
Lynn's garden will be rectangular, with a semicircular flowerbed at one end, and a matching
semicircular patio at the other end. The rest of the space will be taken up by a lawn.

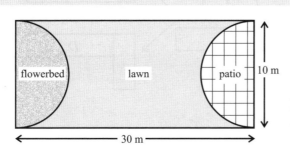

Diagram not
accurately drawn

A of c = πr^2

The grass seed that Lynn is planning to use comes in boxes that cost £7 each.
Each box will cover 10 m². How much will it cost Lynn to plant the lawn?

Rectangle = 30m × 10m = 300m²
Circle = πr^2 = $\pi \times 5^2$ = $\pi 25$
   = 78.54 m²
Lawn = 300 − 78.54 = 221.46 m²

$\dfrac{221.46}{10}$ = 22.146   23 × £7 = £161
     = 23

£ 161 ....

[Total 3 marks]

2 The diagram below shows an isosceles trapezium.

Find the area of the trapezium.

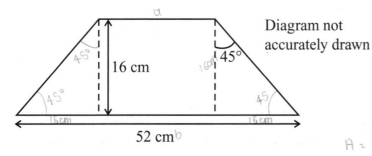

52 cm

Diagram not
accurately drawn

A = $\frac{1}{2}$ (a+b) × h

52 − 16 − 16 = 20
   a = 20 cm

A = 0.5 × (52 + 20) × 16
A = 36 × 16
A = 576

........576...... cm²

[Total 2 marks]

3 Consider a square and a triangle. The sides of the square are *x* cm long.
The base length and height of the triangle are equal, and are twice as long as the
sides of the square. The area of the triangle is 9 cm² larger than the area of the square.

Find the perimeter of the square.

   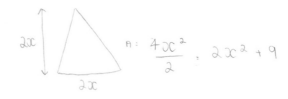

.... cm

[Total 4 marks]

4 Rectangle *B* is twice as long as rectangle *A*. They have the same width.
The two rectangles can be joined to make shape *C*, which has perimeter 28 cm.
They can be joined in a different way to make shape *D*, which has perimeter 34 cm.

Find the perimeters of rectangles *A* and *B*.

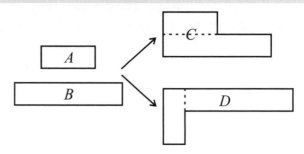

Perimeter of *A*: .... cm

Perimeter of *B*: .... cm

[Total 6 marks]

5 Look at the sector shown in the diagram below.

Diagram not
accurately drawn

30°

6 cm

½
of circle

Find the perimeter and the area of the sector.
Give your answers to 3 significant figures.

PERIMETER · πd = ∙π × (6×2) = 37.6991
                                        ──────── = 3.1415
                                           12

3.14159 + 6 + 6 = 15.14159
                    (3sf)

πr² = π × (6²) = π × 36 = 113.09733
                          ──────────
                              12

= 9.424777
(3sf) = 9.42

Perimeter = ...15.1..... ✓ cm

Area = ...9.42..... ✓ cm²

[Total 5 marks]

6 An industrial rolling machine is made up of three identical cylinders of radius 9 cm.
The ends of the rollers are surrounded by a strip of metal, as illustrated in the diagram below.

Find the length of the metal strip,
giving your answer correct to 1 d.p.

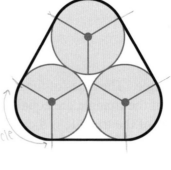

If you're struggling with the
straight bits, try looking at
the horizontal part first.

18cm

π × 18 = 56.548
─────────────── = 18.8495
        3

⅓
of circle

.....110.5 ✓ cm

[Total 4 marks]

curved bits: 18 · 8495 × 3 = 56.548

3 × 18 = 54 + 56.548
        = 110.548

Score:

24

Section Five — Geometry and Measures

3D Shapes — Surface Area and Volume

1   The diagram below shows a wooden spinning top made from a hemisphere and a cone.

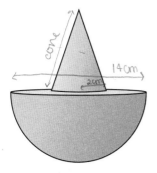

The hemisphere has a diameter of 14 cm.
The slanting length of the cone is 12 cm and the radius of its base is 2 cm.

Work out the total surface area of the spinning top.
Give your answer to 3 significant figures.

.... cm^2
[Total 4 marks]

2   The curved surface of a cone is made from the net below.

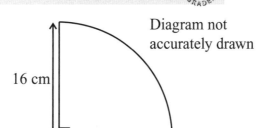

Diagram not
accurately drawn

16 cm

The cone has a circular base.
Calculate the total surface area of the cone. Give your answer in terms of π.

.... cm^2
[Total 5 marks]

3   A spherical ball has volume 478 cm^3.

Find the surface area of the ball, giving your answer correct to 1 d.p.

.... cm^2
[Total 4 marks]

4   The diagram below shows a clay bowl in the shape of a hollow hemisphere.
     The radius of the inside surface is 8 cm. The radius of the outside surface is 9 cm.

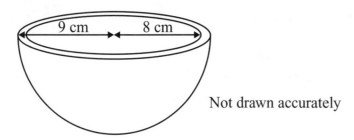

Not drawn accurately

What volume of clay is needed to make the bowl?
Give your answer to 3 significant figures.

.... cm³

[Total 3 marks]

5   The cone and sphere in the diagram below have the same volume.

 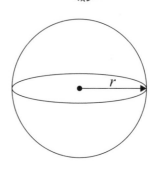

The cone has a vertical height of 18 cm and a base diameter of 12 cm.
Work out the radius, *r*, of the sphere. Give your answer to 3 significant figures.

.... cm

[Total 4 marks]

6   The diagram shows how two identical solid spheres fit **exactly** inside a cuboid box.

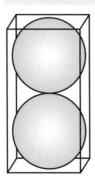

Find the percentage of the volume of the box which is occupied by the spheres.
Give your answer to 1 d.p.

...........................%

[Total 4 marks]

Section Five — Geometry and Measures

7   A farmer is filling a water trough for his cattle. The trough is the shape of a prism with a trapezium as its cross-section, as shown in the diagram below. Water flows into the trough at a rate of 9 litres per minute.

How long will it take to completely fill the trough?

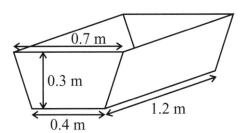

.... minutes

[Total 4 marks]

8   Water is flowing through the cylindrical pipe shown in the diagram below. The radius of the pipe is 0.2 m, and the water comes halfway up the pipe.

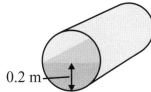

a) Find the cross-sectional area of the water in the pipe.

.... m^2

[1]

The water is flowing at a rate of 2520 litres per minute.

b) Find the speed of the water in m/s to 3 s.f.

Convert rate of flow to m^3/s:

2520 litres/minute = (2520 ÷ ....) litres/second = ... litres/second

= .... cm^3/s

= .... m^3/s

Speed = Rate of flow ÷ cross-sectional area of water

= .... m^3/s ÷ .... m^2

= .... m/s

.... m/s

[4]

[Total 5 marks]

Exam Practice Tip

Rate of flow questions like Q8 can be pretty mind-boggling... Remember that rate of flow in m^3/s just means "volume moved per second". So dividing this by the cross-sectional area gives "distance moved per second" — and that's just speed. Don't rush into it though — make sure your units match up nicely first.

Score

33

More Enlargements

1 The radius of a tennis ball and the radius of a basketball are in the ratio $1:7$. **(7)**

Assuming both balls are spheres, work out the ratio of the volume of a tennis ball to the volume of a basketball.

....

[Total 1 mark]

2 A parallelogram has an area of 7 cm². **(7)**

The parallelogram is enlarged with scale factor 3. Work out the area of the enlarged parallelogram.

.... cm²

[Total 2 marks]

3 Cylinder B is an enlargement of cylinder A.
The ratio of the volume of cylinder A to the volume of cylinder B is $27:64$. **(7)**
The surface area of cylinder A is 81π cm².

Find the surface area of cylinder B.

.... cm²

[Total 3 marks]

4 **A**, **B** and **C** are three solid cones which are mathematically similar. The surface area of each cone is given below. The perpendicular height of **A** is 4 cm. The volume of **C** is 135π cm³. **(7)**

Not to scale

108π cm²

48π cm²

12π cm²

A   **B**   **C**

a) Calculate the volume of **A**.

.... cm³

[4]

b) Calculate the perpendicular height of **B**.

.... cm

[3]

[Total 7 marks]

Score:

13

Section Five — Geometry and Measures

Projections

1 The diagram below shows a solid made from identical cubes.
The side elevation of the solid is drawn on the adjacent grid.

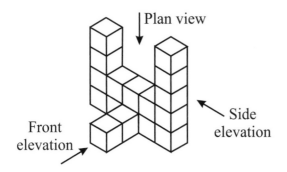

Plan view

Front elevation

Side elevation

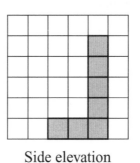

Side elevation

 a) On the grid below, draw the front elevation of the solid. *[1]*

b) On the grid below, draw the plan view of the solid. *[1]*

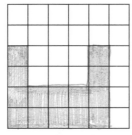 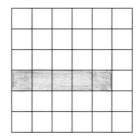

Front elevation Plan view

[Total 2 marks]

2 The diagram shows a house made of a 5 m × 5 m × 6 m cuboid
and a triangular roof of width 4 m, length 5 m and vertical height 4 m.

 On the grid below, draw the front elevation of the house.
Use a scale of 1 square = 1 m.

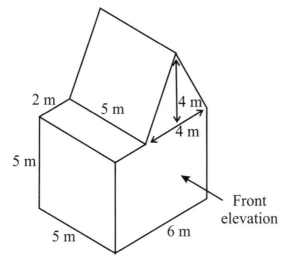

2 m 5 m 4 m

4 m

5 m

Front elevation

5 m 6 m

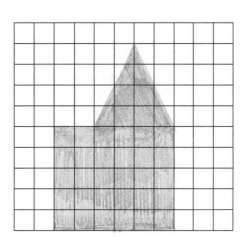

[Total 2 marks]

Score:

4

Section Five — Geometry and Measures

Loci and Construction

1   *EFG* is an isosceles triangle. Sides *EG* and *FG* are both 4.5 cm long. **(3)**

Side *EF* has been drawn here.

    E ——————— F

a) Complete the construction of triangle *EFG* by
   drawing sides *EG* and *FG*.

[2]

b) Construct the bisector of angle *EGF*.

[2]

[Total 4 marks]

2   Rectangle *ABCD* has a perimeter of 18 cm. Side *AB* has been drawn below. **(4)**

Using a ruler and compasses, construct rectangle *ABCD*.

    A ———————————————— B

[Total 4 marks]

3   A dog is tied to a beam *AB* by a lead which allows it to run a maximum of 2 m from the beam. **(4)**

    Shade the region on the diagram where the dog may run, using the scale shown.

Scale: 1 cm
represents 1 m

    A ———————————————— B

[Total 2 marks]

4 *ABC* is a triangle.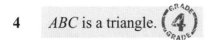

 Find and shade the region inside the triangle which is **both** closer to the line *AB* than the line *BC*, **and** also more than 6.5 cm from the point *C*.

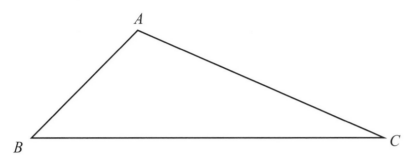

[Total 4 marks]

5 A town council are putting up a new visitor information board. They want it to be placed within the area shown, closer to the park than to the library, but also closer to the station than to the park.

The diagram below shows a scale map of the town centre.
Shade in the region of the town where the board could be placed.

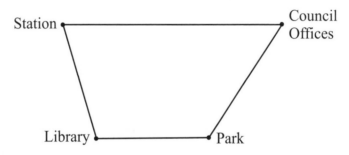

[Total 3 marks]

6 Triangle *XYZ* is shown below. It is rotated 180° clockwise about vertex *X* and then 90° clockwise about vertex *Z*.

Draw the locus of vertex *Y*.

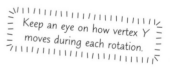

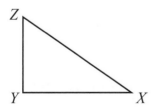

[Total 3 marks]

Score:

20

Bearings

1   Two ships leave a port at the same time.
    Ship *A* travels due west for 40 km. Ship *B* travels 60 km on a bearing of 110°. (3)

    a) Using a scale of 1 cm = 10 km, draw the journeys of the two ships in the space below and clearly
       mark their final positions.

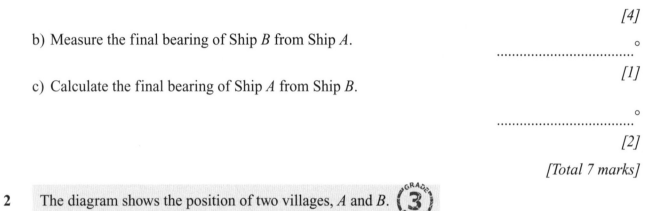

                                                                                                    [4]

    b) Measure the final bearing of Ship *B* from Ship *A*.
                                                                              .... °
                                                                                                    [1]

    c) Calculate the final bearing of Ship *A* from Ship *B*.

                                                                              .... °
                                                                                                    [2]
                                                                                        [Total 7 marks]

2   The diagram shows the position of two villages, *A* and *B*. (3)

    a) A walker hikes from village *A* on a bearing of 035°.
       After an hour's walk he stops when village *B* is directly east of his position.
       Mark the walker's position on the diagram with a cross (×) and label it *W*.

                                                                                                    [2]

    b) Another village, *C*, is on a bearing of 115° from village *A*, and on a bearing of 235° from
       village *B*. Mark the location of village *C* with a cross (×) and label it *C*.
                                                                                                    [3]

    c) Use a protractor to measure the bearing that the walker must hike
       on from his position at *W*, in order to reach village *C*.   .... °
                                                                                                    [1]
                                                                                        [Total 6 marks]

                                                                              Score:

                                                                                        13

Section Five — Geometry and Measures

Pythagoras' Theorem

1 The diagram shows a right-angled triangle ABC.
AC is 4 cm long. BC is 8 cm long.

Calculate the length of AB.
Give your answer to 2 decimal places.

$$a^2 + b^2 = c^2$$
$$4^2 + 8^2 = c^2$$
$$16 + 64 = c^2 \quad c = 8.94427191$$
$$80 = c^2 \quad c = 8.94$$

...........8.94.✓........ cm

[Total 3 marks]

2 Point A has coordinates $(2, -1)$. Point B has coordinates $(8, 8)$.
Find the exact length of the line segment AB. Simplify your answer as much as possible.

....

[Total 3 marks]

3 A triangle has a base of 10 cm. Its other two sides are both 13 cm long.

Calculate the area of the triangle.

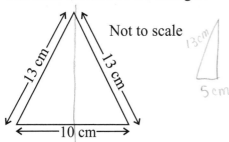

Not to scale

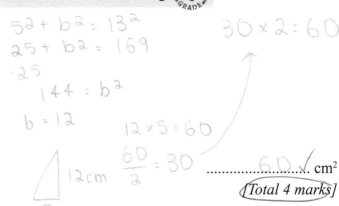

$$5^2 + b^2 = 13^2$$
$$25 + b^2 = 169$$
$$-25$$
$$144 = b^2$$
$$b = 12$$

$$30 \times 2 = 60$$

$$12 \times 5 = 60$$
$$\frac{60}{2} = 30$$

...........60....✓.. cm²

[Total 4 marks]

4 The diagram shows a kite $ABCD$. AB is 28.3 cm long.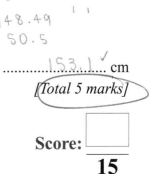
BC is 54.3 cm long. BE is 20 cm in length.

Work out the perimeter of triangle ABC. Give your answer to 1 decimal place.

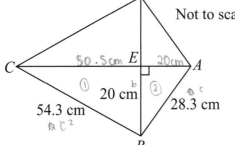

Not to scale

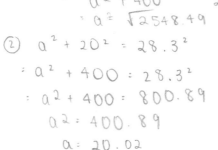

① $a^2 + 20^2 = 54.3^2$
   $400 + a^2 = 54.3^2$
   $a^2 + 400$ 2948.49
   $a = \sqrt{2548.49} = 50.5$

② $a^2 + 20^2 = 28.3^2$
   $a^2 + 400 = 28.3^2$
   $a^2 + 400 = 800.89$
   $a^2 = 400.89$
   $a = 20.02$

$$
\begin{array}{r}
54.3 \\
28.3 \\
20.0 \\
+\ 50.5 \\
\hline
153.1 \\
\end{array}
$$

...........153.1......✓ cm

[Total 5 marks]

Score: ☐

15

Trigonometry

1 The diagram shows a right-angled triangle.

Find the size of the angle marked x.
Give your answer to 1 decimal place.

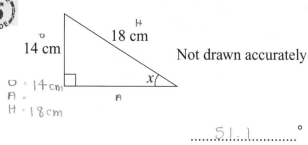

14 cm

Not drawn accurately

$O = 14\,cm$
$A =$
$H = 18\,cm$

$\sin(x) = \dfrac{14\,cm}{18\,cm}$ $S\ ^O_H$

$\sin(x) = \dfrac{7}{9}$ x

$x = \sin^{-1}\left(\dfrac{7}{9}\right)$

..........5.1.1..........°

[Total 3 marks]

2 The diagram shows a right-angled triangle.

Find the exact length of the side marked y.

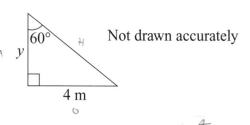

60°

A y

Not drawn accurately

4 m

$O = 4m$
$A = y$
$H = $ _____

$T\ ^O_A$

$A = \dfrac{O}{T}$ $A = \dfrac{4m}{\tan(60)}$

$\dfrac{4}{\sqrt{3}}$

.... m

[Total 3 marks]

3 A regular hexagon is drawn such that all of its vertices
are on the circumference of a circle of radius 8.5 cm.

Calculate the distance from the centre of the circle to the centre of one edge of the hexagon.
Give your answer to 2 decimal places.

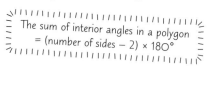
The sum of interior angles in a polygon
= (number of sides − 2) × 180°

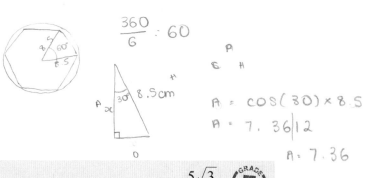

$\dfrac{360}{6} = 60$

A

$\varepsilon\ H$

8.5cm

$A\ \ _{30°}$ x

$A = \cos(30) \times 8.5$

$A = 7.36|12$

$A = 7.36$

..........7.36..✓.... cm

[Total 5 marks]

4 Show that $\tan 30° + \sin 60° = \dfrac{5\sqrt{3}}{6}$

[Total 3 marks]

Score

14

The Sine and Cosine Rules

1 In the triangle below, $AB = 10$ cm, $BC = 7$ cm and angle $ABC = 85°$.

$a^2 = b^2 + c^2 (2bc \cos A)$

a) Calculate the length of AC.
Give your answer to 3 significant figures.

$AC^2 = \underline{7}^2 + \underline{10}^2 - (2 \times \underline{7} \times \underline{10} \times \cos \underline{85}°)$

$AC^2 = \sqrt{\underline{149} - (\underline{140} \times \cos \underline{85}°)}$

$AC^2 = \sqrt{136.7798196}$

$AC = 11.696$ $AC = 11.7$

.........11.7........ cm
[2]

b) Calculate the area of triangle ABC.
Give your answer to 3 significant figures.

$\frac{1}{2} ab \sin C$ $\frac{1}{2} ac \sin B$

$0.5 \times 7 \times 10 \times \sin(85)$

$= 34.866$

.........34.9........ cm²
[2]

[Total 4 marks]

2 In the triangle below, $AB = 12$ cm, $BC = 19$ cm and $AC = 14$ cm.

Calculate the area of the triangle.

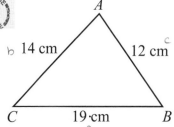

Diagram not accurately drawn

.... cm²
[Total 4 marks]

3 $ABCD$ is a trapezium.

BC is parallel to AD.
$BC = x$ cm.
$AD = 3x$ cm.
Angle $BAC = 30°$.

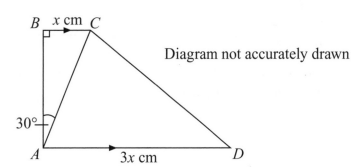

Diagram not accurately drawn

The perimeter of triangle ACD is $(a + \sqrt{b})x$ cm. Find the values of a and b.

$a =$ .... , $b =$ ....
[Total 5 marks]

Section Six — Pythagoras and Trigonometry

4 In the triangle below, $AB = 17$ cm, $AC = 36$ cm and angle $ACB = 26°$
Angle ABC is obtuse.

Find the size of angle ABC. Give your answer to correct to 1 d.p.

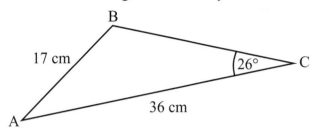

.............................°

[Total 3 marks]

5 A castle drawbridge is supported by two chains, AB and AC. Using the information
on the diagram, calculate the total length of the drawbridge, BD, correct to 3 s.f.

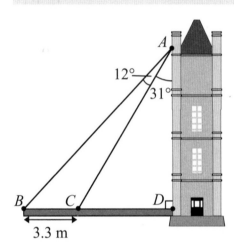

.... m

[Total 5 marks]

6 $ABCD$ is a quadrilateral.

$AB = 55$ cm.
$DC = 84$ cm.
Angle $ABC = 116°$.
Angle $BCD = 78°$.

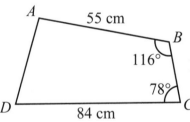

Diagram not accurately drawn

Given that $AC = 93$ cm, work out the area of $ABCD$ to 3 significant figures.
Show clearly how you get your answer.

.... cm^2

[Total 6 marks]

Score:

27

Section Six — Pythagoras and Trigonometry

3D Pythagoras and Trigonometry

1 The diagram below is a cuboid *ABCDEFGH*.

The cuboid has sides of length
6 cm, 4 cm and 3 cm.

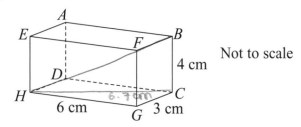

Not to scale

Calculate the length of the diagonal *BH*.
Give your answer to 3 significant figures.

$BH^2 = $ ....² + ...² + ...²

$BH = \sqrt{........}$

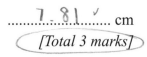

$BH = $ ....

$60.89 = c^2$

$\sqrt{60.89} = c$

$c = 7.81$

$6^2 + 3^2 = c^2$
$36 + 9 = c^2$
$45 = c^2$
$\sqrt{45} = c$
6.7 cm

........7.81✓........ cm

[Total 3 marks]

2 The diagram below is a cuboid *ABCDEFGH*. It represents an empty box with a volume of 80 cm³ and 2 edges measuring 2 cm and 8 cm.

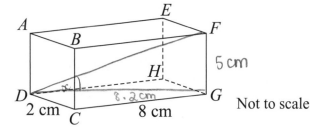

Not to scale

A straight stick is placed in the box and wedged between points *F* and *D*.
Find the size of the angle the stick makes with the plane *CDHG*.
Give your answer to 2 significant figures.

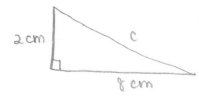

$2^2 + 8^2 = c^2$
$4 + 64 = c^2$
$68 = c^2$
$\sqrt{68} = c$
8.2 cm

$v = 80$
$2 \times 8 \times ? = 80$
$16 \times ? = 80$
$\dfrac{80}{16} = 5$

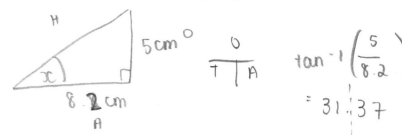

$\dfrac{O}{T \mid A}$

$\tan^{-1}\left(\dfrac{5}{8.2}\right)$

$= 31.37$

........31✓........°

[Total 5 marks]

Score: 8

8

Vectors

1   **a**, **b** and **c** are column vectors, where $\mathbf{a} = \begin{pmatrix} -3 \\ 5 \end{pmatrix}$, $\mathbf{b} = \begin{pmatrix} 5 \\ 4 \end{pmatrix}$ and $\mathbf{c} = \begin{pmatrix} -4 \\ -6 \end{pmatrix}$ **⑤**

Calculate:

a) $\mathbf{a} - \mathbf{b}$

$$\begin{pmatrix} -3 \\ 5 \end{pmatrix} - \begin{pmatrix} 5 \\ 4 \end{pmatrix} = \begin{matrix} -3 - 5 \\ 5 - 4 \end{matrix} = \begin{matrix} -8 \\ 1 \end{matrix}$$

$\begin{pmatrix} -8 \\ 1 \end{pmatrix}$

[1]

b) $4\mathbf{b} - \mathbf{c}$

$$4\begin{pmatrix} 5 \\ 4 \end{pmatrix} = \begin{matrix} 20 \\ 16 \end{matrix} - \begin{matrix} -4 \\ -6 \end{matrix} \quad \begin{matrix} 24 \\ 22 \end{matrix}$$

$\begin{pmatrix} 24 \\ 22 \end{pmatrix}$

[1]

c) $2\mathbf{a} + \mathbf{b} + 3\mathbf{c}$

$$2\begin{pmatrix} -3 \\ 5 \end{pmatrix} + \begin{pmatrix} 5 \\ 4 \end{pmatrix} + 3\begin{pmatrix} -4 \\ -6 \end{pmatrix}$$

$$\begin{matrix} -6 \\ 10 \end{matrix} + \begin{matrix} 5 \\ 4 \end{matrix} + \begin{matrix} -12 \\ -18 \end{matrix} = \begin{matrix} -1 \\ 14 \end{matrix} + \begin{matrix} -12 \\ -18 \end{matrix} = \begin{matrix} -13 \\ -4 \end{matrix}$$

$\begin{pmatrix} -13 \\ -4 \end{pmatrix}$

[1]

[Total 3 marks]

2 ABC is a triangle where $\overrightarrow{AB} = 4\mathbf{a}$ and $\overrightarrow{BC} = 3\mathbf{b}$. P is the <u>midpoint</u> of BC. **⑥**

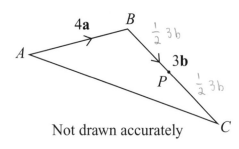

Not drawn accurately

a) Write $\overrightarrow{AC}$ in terms of **a** and **b**.

$\overrightarrow{AC} = \overrightarrow{AB} + \overrightarrow{BC}$

$\overrightarrow{AC} = 4a + 3b$

$\overrightarrow{AC} = 4a + 3b$

[1]

b) Write $\overrightarrow{AP}$ in terms of **a** and **b**.

$\overrightarrow{AP} = 4a + \frac{1}{2}3b$

$\overrightarrow{AP} = 4a + 1.5b$

$\overrightarrow{AP} = 4a + 1.5b$

[1]

[Total 2 marks]

3 $ABCD$ is a parallelogram. $\overrightarrow{AB} = 2\mathbf{a}$ and $\overrightarrow{AD} = 2\mathbf{d}$. **⑥**
L is the midpoint of AC, and M is the midpoint of BC.

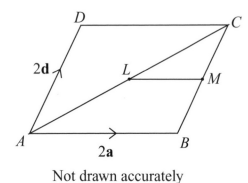

Not drawn accurately

Write in terms of **a** and **d**:

a) $\overrightarrow{CD}$

....

[1]

b) $\overrightarrow{AC}$

....

[1]

c) $\overrightarrow{BL}$

....

[1]

[Total 3 marks]

4 In the diagram, $\overrightarrow{OA} = 2\mathbf{a}$ and $\overrightarrow{OB} = \mathbf{b}$.
M is the midpoint of AB.

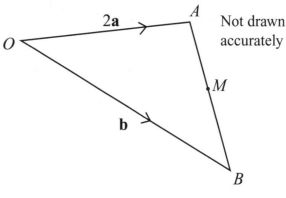

Not drawn accurately

a) Find $\overrightarrow{OM}$ in terms of **a** and **b**. (**7**)

$\overrightarrow{OM} = \underline{\quad} + \underline{\quad} = \underline{\quad} + \frac{1}{2}\underline{\quad}$

$\overrightarrow{AB} = \underline{\quad} + \underline{\quad}$

$\overrightarrow{OM} = \underline{\quad} + \frac{1}{2}(\underline{\quad}) = \underline{\quad}$

....
[2]

X is a point on AB such that $AX:XB = 1:3$. (**9**)

b) Find $\overrightarrow{OX}$ in terms of **a** and **b**.

....
[3]

[Total 5 marks]

5 ABCD is a parallelogram. $\overrightarrow{AB} = 3\mathbf{a}$, and $\overrightarrow{BW} = \mathbf{b}$. (**9**)

M is the midpoint of CD and $AX = 2XC$.
$BW:WC = 1:5$

a) Find $\overrightarrow{BX}$ in terms of **a** and **b**.

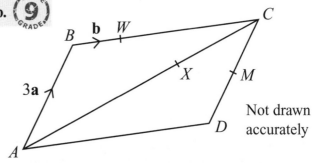

Not drawn accurately

....
[4]

b) Hence show that B, X and M are three points on a straight line.

[4]

[Total 8 marks]

Score:

21

Section Six — Pythagoras and Trigonometry

Probability Basics

1   Amy has a bag containing strawberry and banana sweets in the ratio $2:5$. She picks a sweet at random from the bag.

　　a) What is the probability that she picks a <u>strawberry</u> sweet from the bag?

$$\frac{2}{7}$$

$$\frac{2}{7}$$
....
[1]

b) Amy says, "I am exactly twice as likely to pick a banana sweet as a strawberry sweet". Is Amy correct? Explain your answer.

....

....
[2]

[Total 3 marks]

2   There are p counters in a bag. n of the counters are blue and the rest are red. One counter is picked out at random.

Work out the probability that the counter picked is red.
Give your answer as a fraction in terms of p and n.

....
[Total 2 marks]

3   Arthur has stripy, spotty and plain socks in his drawer. He picks a sock from the drawer at random.

The probability of picking a plain sock is 0.4, and of picking a spotty sock is y.
He is twice as likely to pick a stripy sock as a spotty sock.
Find the value of y. Give your answer as a decimal.

P(stripy sock) = ... y

.... $+ y +$ .... $= 1$

.... $= 0.6$

$y =$ ....

$y =$ ....
[Total 3 marks]

Score: ☐

8

Counting Outcomes

1 Alvar has a fair six sided dice and a set of five cards numbered 2, 4, 6, 8 and 10.
He rolls the dice and chooses a card at random.
Alvar adds the number on the dice to the number on the card to calculate his total score.

 Find the probability that Alvar will score more than 4.

....

[Total 3 marks]

2 A shop sells three different meal deals. The possible meal deal options are:
  • sandwich and drink • sandwich and snack • sandwich, snack and drink

There are 5 different sandwiches, 8 different drinks and 4 different snacks.
How many possible meal deal combinations are there?

$5 \times 8 \times 4$
$= 160$

..........160..........

[Total 3 marks]

3 Trish spins 5 fair spinners, each numbered 1-4. She writes down, in order, the number that each spinner lands on to generate a 5 digit number.

a) How many different possibilities are there for the 5 digit number she generates?

....

[1]

b) What is the probability of Trish generating a 5 digit number not containing a 1?

....

[2]

[Total 3 marks]

4 A row of six disco lights all flash at the same time.
Each light randomly flashes either red, blue, green or yellow.

a) How many possible colour combinations of the six lights are there?

$4 \times 6 = 24$

..........24..........

[1]

b) What is the probability that, in one flash, all the lights are either red or blue?

....

[2]

[Total 3 marks]

Score: ☐

12

Section Seven — Probability and Statistics

Probability Experiments

1   Suda has a six-sided dice. The sides are numbered 1 to 6.

Suda rolls the dice 50 times. Her results are shown in the table below.

Number	1	2	3	4	5	6
Relative Frequency	0.32	0.12	0.24	0.14	0.06	0.12

a) How many times did she roll a 6?

$$\frac{12}{100} = \frac{6}{50}$$

......................6......

[2]

b) Is Suda's dice fair? Explain your answer.

.....Yes...all the relative frequencies add to 1.................................

....

[2]

c) She rolls the dice another 50 times. Should she expect the same results? Explain your answer.

.....No because the die is random and therefore has no..........

.......pattern...

[1]

[Total 5 marks]

2   Eimear has a bag containing a large number of counters.
Each counter is numbered either 1, 2, 3, 4 or 5.

She selects one counter from the bag, makes a note of its number, and then puts it back in the bag.
Eimear does this 100 times. Her results are shown in the table below.

Number on counter	1	2	3	4	5
Frequency	23	25	22	21	9
Relative Frequency					

a) Complete the table, giving the relative frequencies of each counter being selected.

[2]

b) Elvin says that he thinks that the bag contains the same number of counters with each number.
Do you agree? Give a reason for your answer.

....

[1]

c) Using Eimear's results, estimate the probability of selecting an odd number
when one counter is picked from the bag.

....

[2]

[Total 5 marks]

Section Seven — Probability and Statistics

3 Danielle thinks she can predict if a fair coin will land showing heads or tails.

a) She makes a prediction and flips the coin. She repeats this 8 times.
The results are shown in the table below.

Prediction	H	H	T	H	T	H	H	H
Outcome	H	T	H	H	T	H	H	T

  i) How many predictions would you expect to be correct if she was just guessing?

....

[1]

  ii) Do you think Danielle can predict the flip of a coin? Explain your answer.

....

....

[1]

Danielle flipped the coin another 100 times and predicted the outcome of each flip.
She predicted it would land showing heads 39 times. It landed on tails 53 times.
Of the times it landed on tails, 3 more of her predictions were correct than were wrong.

b) i) Complete the frequency tree below to show these results.

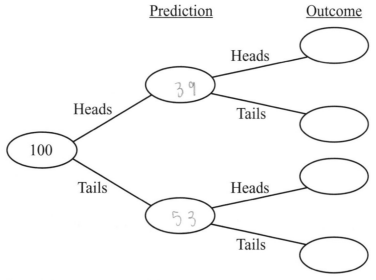

[3]

  ii) Work out the relative frequency of Danielle predicting the outcome correctly.

....

[2]

c) Are the results from the experiment in part a) or part b) more reliable? Explain your answer.

....

....

[1]

[Total 8 marks]

Score:

18

Section Seven — Probability and Statistics

The AND / OR Rules

1   A biased 5-sided spinner is numbered 1-5.

The probability that the spinner will land on each of the numbers 1 to 5 is given in this table.

Number	1	2	3	4	5
Probability	0.3	0.15	0.2	0.25	0.1

a) What is the probability of the spinner landing on a prime number or a multiple of 2? **(6)**

....

[2]

b) The spinner is spun until it lands on a 2.
   i) What is the probability that the spinner is spun exactly twice? **(7)**

....

[2]

   ii) Work out the probability that the spinner is spun more than twice. **(7)**

....

[2]

[Total 6 marks]

2   Shaun is playing the game 'hook-a-duck'. The probability that he wins a prize is 0.3, independent of what has happened in previous games.

a) If he plays three games, what is the probability that he doesn't win a prize? **(6)**

....

[1]

b) If he plays two games, what is the probability that he wins at least one prize? **(7)**

....

[2]

c) Shaun says, "if I play three games I have more than a 50% chance of winning exactly one prize". Is he correct? Explain your answer. **(8)**

....

....

[3]

[Total 6 marks]

Exam Practice Tip

You can't just use the AND / OR rules mindlessly, you need to do a bit of thinking about the events before you start any questions. If you're using the OR rule you need to check if the events can happen at the same time or not. If you're using the AND rule you'll have to check that the events are independent.

Score

12

Section Seven — Probability and Statistics

Tree Diagrams

1 Jo and Heather are meeting for coffee.
The probability that Jo will wear burgundy trousers is $\frac{2}{5}$.
There is a one in four chance that Heather will wear burgundy trousers.
The two events are independent.

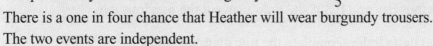

a) Complete the tree diagram below.

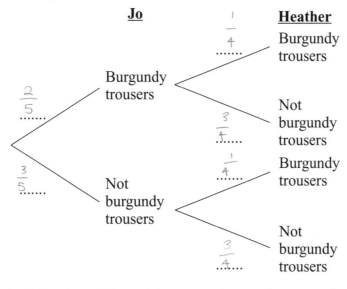

Jo   **Heather**

$\frac{2}{5}$ Burgundy trousers

$\frac{1}{4}$ Burgundy trousers

$\frac{3}{4}$ Not burgundy trousers

$\frac{3}{5}$ Not burgundy trousers

$\frac{1}{4}$ Burgundy trousers

$\frac{3}{4}$ Not burgundy trousers

[2]

b) What is the probability that neither of them wear burgundy trousers?

$$\frac{3}{5} \times \frac{3}{4} = \frac{9}{20}$$

$\frac{9}{20}$ ....

[2]

[Total 4 marks]

2 Paul and Jen play a game where they roll a fair dice. If it lands on a factor of 6 then Paul gets a point, otherwise Jen gets a point. The winner is the person who gets the most points.

a) If they roll the dice twice, what is the probability that it will be a draw?

....

[3]

b) If they roll the dice three times, what is the probability that Paul wins?

....

[3]

[Total 6 marks]

Score:

10

        Section Seven — Probability and Statistics

Conditional Probability

1   The probability that Gemma has pasta for dinner depends on whether she had pasta the previous day. The probability that she will have pasta for dinner is 0.3 if she had it the previous day and 0.8 if she didn't have it the previous day.

a) Given that Gemma had pasta today, complete the tree diagram below.

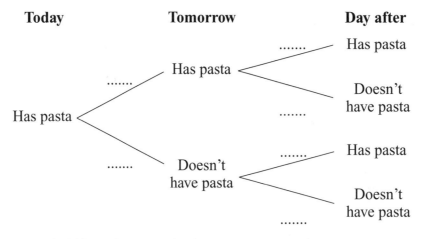

[2]

b) What is the probability of Gemma having pasta on exactly one of the next two days if she had pasta today?

....
[2]
[Total 4 marks]

2   A box of chocolates contains 12 chocolates. 7 are milk chocolate and 5 are white chocolate. Two chocolates are chosen at random without replacement.

a) Given that the first chocolate is a milk chocolate, what is the probability that the second chocolate is a milk chocolate?

....
[1]

b) Calculate the probability of at least one milk chocolate being chosen.

....
[2]

c) Calculate the probability that one milk chocolate and one white chocolate are chosen in any order.

....
[2]
[Total 5 marks]

Score: ▢
9

Section Seven — Probability and Statistics

Sets and Venn Diagrams

1 The Venn diagram below shows the number of elements in sets *A* and *B*.

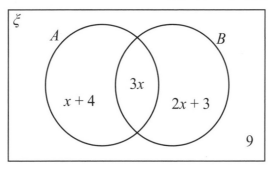

a) Given that n(ξ) = 40, find the value of *x*.

$9 + x + 4 + 3x + 2x + 3 = 40$ $x = 4$
$6x + 16 = 40$
$6x = 24$

$x = \underline{4}$

[2]

b) An element is randomly chosen from the universal set, ξ.
Find P(A ∩ B).

$\dfrac{3x}{40}$ $\dfrac{12}{40} = \dfrac{3}{10}$

$\underline{^3/_{10}}$

[2]

[Total 4 marks]

2 At a football match the probability of a randomly selected member of the crowd buying a pie is 0.33, buying a drink is 0.64 and buying both is 0.27.

a) Find the probability that a randomly selected member of the crowd doesn't buy anything.

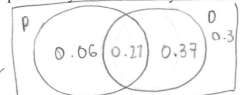

$\underline{0.3}$

[2]

b) 4000 people attend a match. Use a Venn diagram to represent the expected number of people who buy pies, drinks, both or neither at the match.

[3]

c) Find the probability that a randomly selected member of the crowd buys a pie, given that they **don't** buy a drink.

0.06

$\underline{0.06}$

[2]

[Total 7 marks]

3 The Venn diagram below shows the percentages of
female contestants (F) and singers (S) in a talent competition.

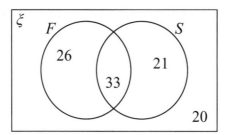

Find the probability that a randomly selected contestant is a male, given that they're a singer.

....

[Total 2 marks]

4 A cheese stall sells three different cheeses: Cheddar, Wensleydale and Stilton.
One afternoon the stall had 100 customers. Each customer bought at least one cheese.

28 customers bought Wensleydale. Of these, 12 customers also bought Stilton.
43 customers bought Cheddar. Of these, 10 also bought Wensleydale and 7 also bought Stilton.
5 customers bought all three cheeses.

a) Draw a Venn diagram to show this information.

[3]

b) Find the probability that a randomly selected customer bought Cheddar or Stilton.

....

[1]

c) Given that a customer bought Wensleydale,
find the probability that this customer also bought Stilton.

....

[2]

[Total 6 marks]

Score:

19

Section Seven — Probability and Statistics

Sampling and Data Collection

1   Faye is investigating how many chocolate bars teenagers buy each week.
   She is going to collect data by asking her teenage friends how many they buy.

a) Design a table that Faye could use to record her data. **(3)**

[2]

b) Comment on whether she can use her results to draw conclusions about teenagers in the UK. **(4)**

....

....

....

[2]

[Total 4 marks]

2   Mario asked 50 people at a football match how they travelled there. He found
   that 22 of them travelled by car. There were 5000 people at the match altogether. **(4)**

a) Use the information above to estimate the number of people who travelled to the match by car.

....

[3]

b) Daisy was at a different football match on the same day. She uses Mario's sample data to estimate that 374 of the 850 people at her match travelled there by car.
   Explain the assumption Daisy has made and comment on the reliability of her estimate.

....

....

....

[2]

[Total 5 marks]

Remember, to get reliable estimates, a sample
needs to fairly represent the population.

Score:

9

Mean, Median, Mode and Range

1 A bakery records the number of cookies it sells each day for ten days. The mean number is 17 and the median number is 15.

 The next day the bakery sells 18 cookies.

a) Is the mean number sold over all eleven days higher than 17? Explain your answer.

....

[1]

b) Is the median number sold over all eleven days higher than 15? Explain your answer.

....

[1]

[Total 2 marks]

2 Lee has 6 pygmy goats. Their weights, in kg, are listed below.

32   23   31   28   36   26

a) Which three weights, from the list above, would have a range which is half the value of the median of the three weights? Write down the range and median with your answer.

.................., ..., ...

range = ..., median = ...

[2]

b) Two of the goats wander off and don't return. The mean weight of the herd is now 27.25 kg. Find the weights of the two goats who wandered off.

.... kg and .... kg

[3]

[Total 5 marks]

3 Show that the difference between the mean and the median of five consecutive integers is always zero.

 Call the five consecutive integers n, n + 1, ..., ... and ....

Median = middle value = ...

$$\text{Mean} = \frac{n + (n + 1) + \rule{1.5cm}{0.4pt} + \rule{1.5cm}{0.4pt} + \rule{1.5cm}{0.4pt}}{\rule{1.5cm}{0.4pt}} = \frac{\rule{1.5cm}{0.4pt}}{\rule{1.5cm}{0.4pt}} = \rule{1.5cm}{0.4pt}$$

Difference between mean and median = ...

[Total 3 marks]

Exam Practice Tip

Questions on the mean aren't usually as straightforward as calculating its value from a list of numbers. No, I'm afraid that won't cut the mustard. You have to figure out how to use the information you're given — e.g. if you know the mean and the number of values, you can easily find the total of all the values.

Score

10

Grouped Frequency Tables

1 During a science experiment 10 seeds were planted and their growth measured to the nearest cm after 12 days. The results were recorded in the table below.

Growth in cm	Number of plants
$0 \leq x \leq 2$	2
$3 \leq x \leq 5$	4
$6 \leq x \leq 8$	3
$9 \leq x \leq 11$	1

Use the table to find:

a) the modal class,

....

[1]

b) the class which contains the median,

....

[1]

c) an estimate of the mean growth.

You can add columns to the table to help you.

.... cm

[4]

[Total 6 marks]

2 The table shows the times it took 32 pupils at a school to run a 200 m sprint.

Time (t seconds)	Frequency
$22 < t \leq 26$	4
$26 < t \leq 30$	8
$30 < t \leq 34$	13
$34 < t \leq 38$	6
$38 < t \leq 42$	1

a) Calculate an estimate for the mean time.

.... seconds

[4]

b) What percentage of pupils got a time of more than 30 seconds?

.........................%

[2]

c) Explain whether you could use the results in the table above to draw conclusions about how long it takes 16-year-old boys at the school to run 200 m.

....

[1]

[Total 7 marks]

Score:

13

Section Seven — Probability and Statistics

Box Plots

1 Rachel and Harry record the distance they cycle each week for 26 weeks.
The box plot below shows information about Rachel's cycling.
The table on the right gives information about Harry's cycling.

Rachel:

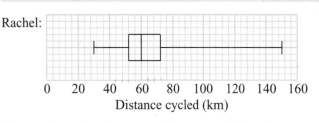

Harry's data	Distance cycled (km)
Shortest distance	0
Lower quartile	32
Median	50
Upper quartile	80
Furthest distance	128

a) Work out the interquartile range of the distances Rachel cycled.

$$72 - 52 = 20$$

...........20.......... km

[2]

b) Explain why the interquartile range might be a better measure
of the spread of Rachel's distances than the range.

....

....

[1]

c) Use the grid opposite to draw a
box plot showing Harry's data.

Harry:

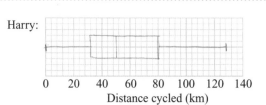

[2]

d) Rachel says that the distances she cycled were more consistent than the distances Harry cycled.
Do you agree with her? Explain your answer.

......Yes, because the spread of distances is less....................................

....

[2]

[Total 7 marks]

2 Tom gives a puzzle to a sample of boys and girls.
These box plots show information about the
time it took the children to finish the puzzle.

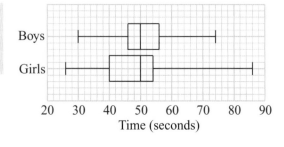

 Compare the distributions of the times taken
by the boys and the times taken by the girls.

....

....

....

[Total 2 marks]

Exam Practice Tip

Even in maths, you sometimes have to answer questions in sentences — but don't forget to show values or
calculations to support your answer. Use the number of marks as a guide as to how much detail to go into.
E.g. if there are two marks available for comparing data sets, you need to make two comparisons.

Score

9

Section Seven — Probability and Statistics

Cumulative Frequency

1 120 pupils in a year group sit an examination at the end of the year.
Their results are given in the table below.

Exam mark (%)	$0 < x \le 20$	$20 < x \le 30$	$30 < x \le 40$	$40 < x \le 50$	$50 < x \le 60$	$60 < x \le 70$	$70 < x \le 80$	$80 < x \le 100$
Frequency	3	10	12	24	42	16	9	4

a) Complete the cumulative frequency table below.

Exam mark (%)	≤ 20	≤ 30	≤ 40	≤ 50	≤ 60	≤ 70	≤ 80	≤ 100
Cumulative Frequency	3	13	25	49	91	107	116	120

[1]

b) Use your table to draw a cumulative frequency graph on the graph paper.

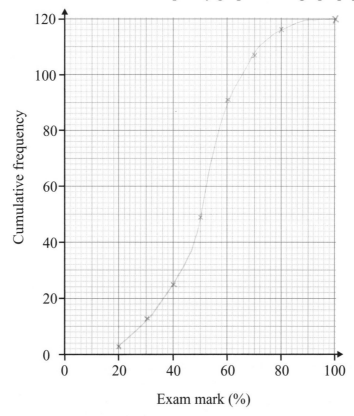

[3]

c) Use your graph to find an estimate for the median.

.... %
[1]

d) Use your graph to find an estimate for the inter-quartile range.

.... %
[2]

e) Each pupil was awarded a grade based on their mark. 4 times as many pupils achieved grade 5 or higher as those who got a lower grade. Estimate the lowest mark needed to get grade 5.

....

....

[3]
[Total 10 marks]

2 The cumulative frequency graph below gives information about the length of time it takes to travel between Udderston and Trundle on the main road each morning. The graph has been drawn using the data from a grouped frequency table.

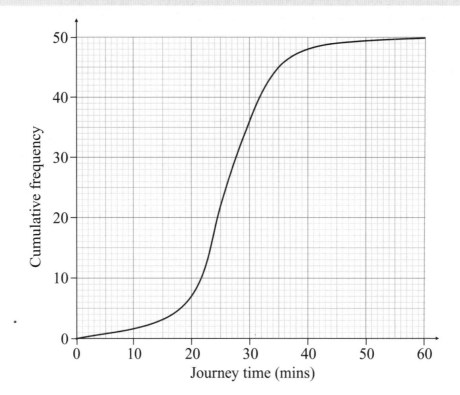

a) Use the graph to estimate:

i) the number of journeys that took between 27 and 47 minutes.

.... *journeys*
[2]

ii) the percentage of journeys that took longer than 40 minutes.

.... %
[2]

b) Explain why your answers to part a) above are only estimates.

....

....
[1]

The minimum journey time was 12 minutes and the maximum journey time was 52 minutes.

c) Using this information and the graph above, draw a box plot on the grid below to show the morning journey times between Udderston and Trundle.

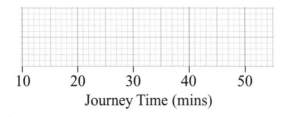

[3]

[Total 8 marks]

Score:

18

Histograms and Frequency Density

1   A group of pupils were each given a potato. The table below gives some information about how long it took the pupils to peel their potato.

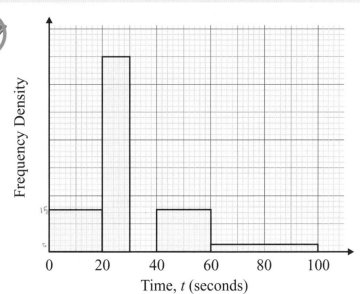

Time, t (seconds)

Time, t (s)	Frequency
$0 < t \le 20$	15
$20 < t \le 30$	
$30 < t \le 40$	30
$40 < t \le 60$	15
$60 < t \le 100$	5

Don't forget to fill in the scale on the frequency density axis.

Fill in the missing entry from the table and complete the histogram.

[Total 3 marks]

2   The histogram shows the amount of time (in minutes) that 270 children spent watching television one evening.

A large sample of adults were asked how long they watched television for on the same evening. The mean time for the adults was 102 minutes.

Does the data shown support the hypothesis that, on average, adults watched more television than children on this particular evening?

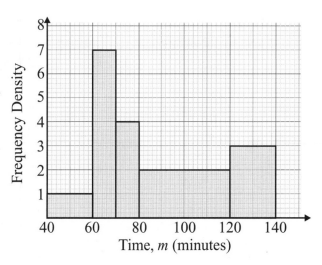

Time, m (minutes)

....

....

....

Make sure you show calculations to support your conclusion.

[Total 4 marks]

Section Seven — Probability and Statistics

3 The histogram shows information about the weights, w kg, of 100 newborn lambs.

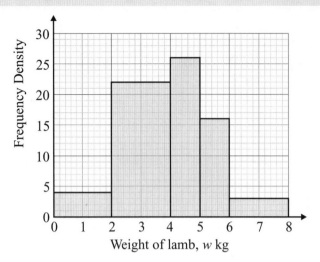

a) Calculate an estimate of the percentage of lambs weighing more than 3.5 kg.

.... %
[3]

b) This table shows information about the weights of the newborn lambs at a different farm.

Weight, w kg	$0 < w \leq 2$	$2 < w \leq 4$	$4 < w \leq 5$	$5 < w \leq 6$	$6 < w \leq 8$
Frequency	4	28	30	28	10

Draw a histogram on the grid to show this data.

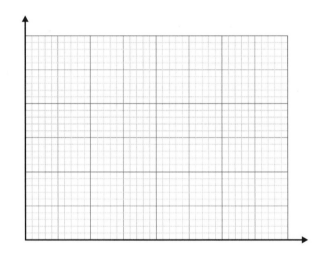

[3]

c) Compare the weights of newborn lambs for the two farms.

....

....

[1]

This question is only worth 1 mark, so you don't need to do any complicated calculations.

[Total 7 marks]

Score:

14

Section Seven — Probability and Statistics

Time Series and Scatter Graphs

1 The numbers of swallows seen in Bluebell Wood over three years are shown in the table.

Year	2010				2011				2012			
Month	Jan	Apr	Jul	Oct	Jan	Apr	Jul	Oct	Jan	Apr	Jul	Oct
No. of swallows	0	60	44	13	0	57	36	10	0	56	34	6

The first eight four-point moving averages for the data have been plotted on the time series graph opposite.

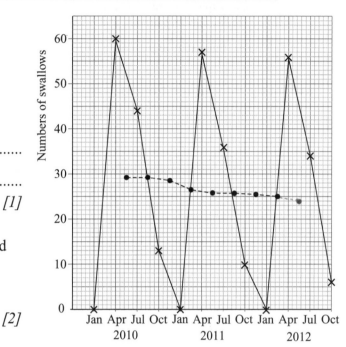

a) Give one reason why a four-point moving average has been used.

...... Four months are displayed ......

....

[1]

b) Calculate the missing moving average and plot the value on the graph.

[2]

c) Describe the overall trend in the numbers of swallows seen.

...... As the years go by, the number of swallows seen slowly decreases.

....

[1]

[Total 4 marks]

2 15 pupils in a class study both Spanish and Italian. Their end of year exam results are shown on the scatter graph below.

a) Circle the point that doesn't follow the trend.

[1]

b) Describe the strength and type of correlation shown by the points that do follow the trend.

...... strong positive correlation

....

[1]

c) Draw a line of best fit for the data.

[1]

[Total 3 marks]

3 A furniture company is looking at how effective their advertising is.
They are comparing how much they spent on advertising in random months with
their total sales value for that month. This information is shown on the graph below.

The table shows the amount spent on advertising and the value of sales for three more months.

Amount spent on advertising (thousands of pounds)	0.75	0.15	1.85
Sales (thousands of pounds)	105	60	170

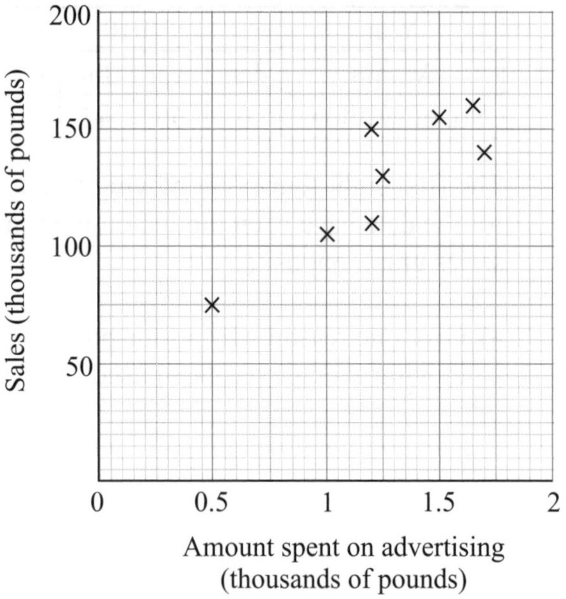

a) Plot the information from the table
   on the scatter graph.

   [1]

b) Describe the relationship between the amount
   spent on advertising and the value of sales.

   ....

   ....

   ....

   [1]

c) Use a line of best fit to estimate how much the company would be likely to spend on advertising
   in a month where they sold £125 000 worth of furniture.

   £ ....

   [2]

d) Use your graph to estimate the monthly sales value if the company spends £600 on advertising.

   £ ....

   [1]

e) The company plan to increase their monthly spend on advertising to at least £3000.
   They use the trend in the data above to predict future sales values.
   Comment on how reliable this prediction is likely to be.

   ....

   ....

   ....

   [2]

   [Total 7 marks]

   Score: ☐

   14

Candidate Surname				Candidate Forename(s)	
Centre Number			Candidate Number		Candidate Signature

GCSE

Mathematics   **Higher Tier**
Paper 1 (Non-Calculator)

Practice Paper
Time allowed: 1 hour 30 minutes

You must have:
Pen, pencil, eraser, ruler, protractor, pair of compasses.
You may use tracing paper.

You are not allowed to use a calculator.

Instructions to candidates
- Use **black** ink to write your answers.
- Write your name and other details in the spaces provided above.
- Answer **all** questions in the spaces provided.
- In calculations show clearly how you worked out your answers.
- Do all rough work on the paper.

Information for candidates
- The marks available are given in brackets at the end of each question.
- You may get marks for method, even if your answer is incorrect.
- There are 24 questions in this paper. There are no blank pages.
- There are 80 marks available for this paper.

Answer ALL the questions.

Write your answers in the spaces provided.

You must show all of your working.

1   A is 60% of B.
      B is 30% of C.

      What percentage of C is A? Circle the correct answer.

      18%   28%   30%   90%

[Total 1 mark]

---

2   Circle the graphs that match the following descriptions.

      (a)   A straight line has equation $y = mx + c$ where $m > 0$ and $c < 0$.

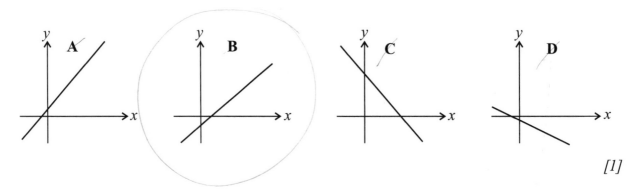

[1]

      (b) y is inversely proportional to x.

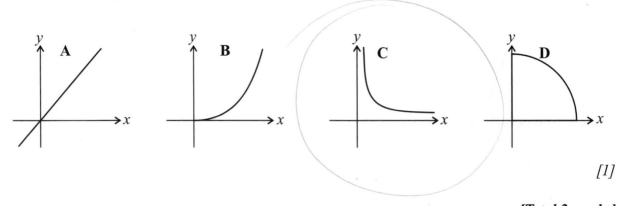

[1]

[Total 2 marks]

1

3 Find 27.68×4.6

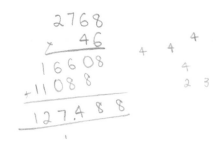

$$2768$$
$$\times \quad 46$$
$$16608$$
$$+11088$$
$$127.488$$

.......127.488......

[Total 3 marks]

---

4 Simplify $\frac{20x^6}{4x^2}$.

Circle the correct answer.

$5x^8$ $5x^3$ $16x^4$ $\boxed{5x^4}$

[Total 1 mark]

---

5 A solid shape has a volume of 2680 mm³.

What is its volume in cm³? Circle the correct answer.

268 cm³ $\boxed{26.8\ cm^3}$ 2.68 cm³   0.268 cm³

1mm   1mm : 1mm³

1mm

[Total 1 mark]

---

6 Estimate the value of

$$\sqrt[3]{\frac{785.3 \times 2.156}{0.1972}}$$

$20 \times 20 \times 20 =$

Show the numbers you used to work out your estimate.

$$\sqrt[3]{\frac{800 \times 2}{0.2}} = \sqrt[3]{\frac{1600}{0.2}} = \sqrt[3]{8000}$$

$$= 20$$

............20...........

[Total 3 marks]

7 The diagram shows a square *EFGH*.
The square has been divided into smaller squares and isosceles triangles.

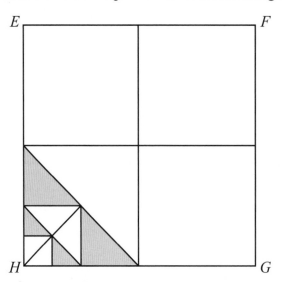

What fraction of the square *EFGH* has been shaded?

....

[Total 3 marks]

---

8 The *n*th term of a sequence is given by the formula $n^2 + 2n + 5$

(a) Fran says "The 4th term in the sequence is a prime number."
Is Fran correct? Tick a box.

Yes ☑   No ☐

Show how you worked out your answer.

$4^2 + 2(4) + 5 = 16 + 8 + 5 = 29$ 29 is prime, so she is correct

[2]

(b) A different sequence begins 2, 5, 7, 12, 19, ...
Write down the next two terms in the sequence.

$12 + 19 =$

$\begin{array}{r} 12 \\ +19 \\ \hline 31 \end{array}$

$\begin{array}{r} 31 \\ +19 \\ \hline 50 \end{array}$

......31..... and ....50...

[2]

[Total 4 marks]

---

9 $\xi = \{1, 2, 3, \ldots, 10\}$
   $A = \{x : 2 < x \le 6\}$
   $B = \{x : x \text{ is a factor of } 12\}$

Complete the Venn diagram to show the elements of each set.

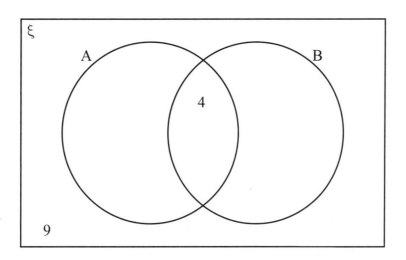

10 (a) Find values of a and b such that

$3a + 2b = 17$ $(\times 2)$
$2a + b = 10$ $(\times 3)$

$6a + 4b = 34$
$6a + 3b = 30$
_____
       $b = 4$

$2a + b = 10$
   $a = 3$

   17
   $\times 2$ 1
   34

$a =$ ....3..........

$b =$ ....4..........

[3]

(b) Hence, work out $a\begin{pmatrix} 2 \\ 1 \end{pmatrix} - b\begin{pmatrix} 3 \\ 2 \end{pmatrix}$

....

[2]

[Total 5 marks]

4

Practice Paper 1

11 The scale drawing shows the position of three hospitals, *A*, *B* and *C*, on an island.

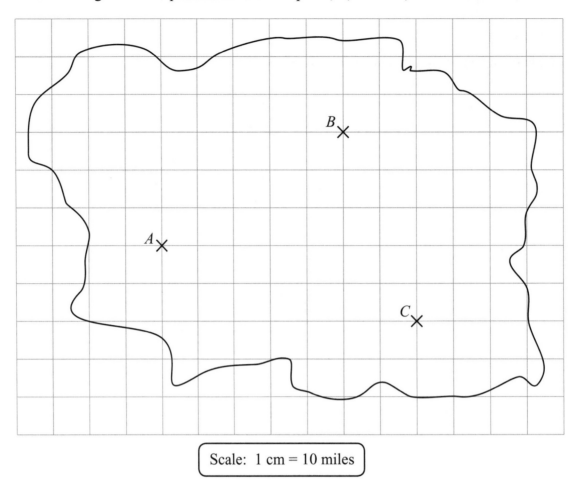

Scale: 1 cm = 10 miles

An ambulance takes a patient to hospital *A* if they are within a 30 mile radius of this hospital.
Otherwise it will take the patient to hospital *B* or *C* depending on which is closer.

Sara calls from her home for an ambulance.
The ambulance takes her to hospital *B*.

Show on the map the region where Sara could live.

[Total 3 marks]

12 $p = 2^3 \times 3^2 \times 5 \times 7$ $q = \frac{6}{7}p$ $r = \frac{4}{15}p$

Work out the highest common factor of *q* and *r*.

....

[Total 3 marks]

5

13 Find $(4 \times 10^6) \times (8 \times 10^{-3})$.
Give your answer in standard form.

....

[Total 2 marks]

14 A block of wood with a weight of 72 N is resting on a horizontal table top.
The base of the block is flat and has area 120 cm².

Find the pressure exerted by the block on the table, giving your answer in N/m².

.... N/m²

[Total 2 marks]

15 A museum bought a valuable painting in January 2013.

In January 2014 the painting was worth 10% more than when the museum bought it.
In January 2015 the painting was worth 30% less than in January 2014.

A newspaper report said: "Overall, the value of the painting decreased by 20%
                              between January 2013 and January 2015."

Was the newspaper correct? Expain your answer.

....

....

....

....

....

[Total 2 marks]

16 The diagram shows a circle A and a sector B.

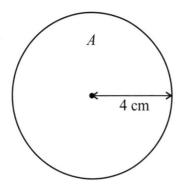

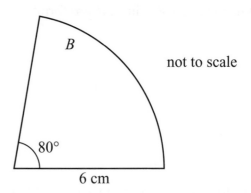

not to scale

Show that the area of A is twice the area of B.

[Total 3 marks]

17 Calculate $\left(2\frac{1}{4}\right)^{-\frac{1}{2}} \div \frac{2}{9}$

....

[Total 4 marks]

7

18 Sixty teams took part in a charity pram race in 2014.
The cumulative frequency graph shows the times that the teams took to complete the course.

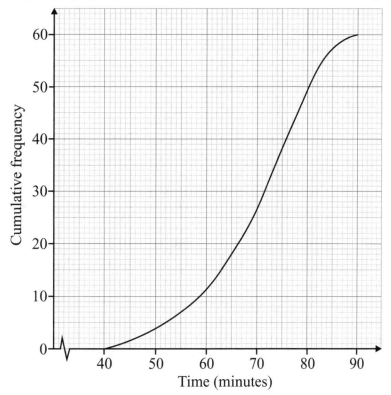

The table below summarises the times that teams took to complete the pram race in 2013.

2013 Pram Race Times	
Median	76 minutes
Interquartile range	18 minutes
Winning time	37 minutes

(a) What is the smallest possible difference between the winning times in 2013 and 2014?

.... minutes

[2]

(b) On average were the teams faster in 2013 or 2014? Explain your answer.

....

....

....

[2]

(c) Were the times more consistent in 2013 or 2014? Explain your answer.

....

....

....

[2]

[Total 6 marks]

19 The diagram shows the temperature, T °C, of a cup of tea m minutes after it is made.

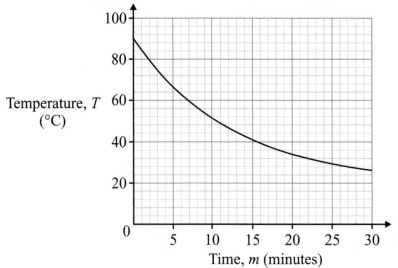

(a) Use the graph to find how long it takes for the temperature of the tea to drop to 32 °C.

.... minutes

[1]

(b) Estimate the rate at which the temperature of the tea is decreasing 10 minutes after it is made.

.... °C/minute

[3]

[Total 4 marks]

20 Write $\dfrac{6}{\sqrt{3}} + \sqrt{27}$ in the form $k\sqrt{3}$.

....

[Total 3 marks]

21

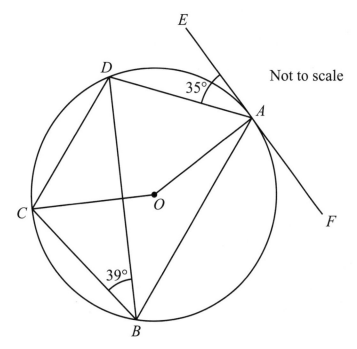

Not to scale

A, B, C and D are points on the circumference of a circle centre O.
EF is a tangent to the circle at A.
Angle $EAD = 35°$ and angle $DBC = 39°$

Work out the size of angle DCO.
Show all of your working, some of which may be on the diagram.

[Total 5 marks]

22 Object A is accelerating. The speed, x m/s, of object A after t seconds ($t > 0$) can be found using the equation $x = \dfrac{18(s + 2t^2)}{5t}$, where s metres is the distance travelled after t seconds.

(a) Rearrange this equation to make s the subject.

$s =$ ....

[2]

(b) A second object, B, travels s metres in t seconds so that:
- s is directly proportional to the square of t.
- it travels 160 metres in 8 seconds.

After 6 seconds the two objects have travelled the same distance.
Calculate the value of x at this time.

$x =$ ....

[5]

[Total 7 marks]

23 (a) Expand $(n + 1)(n - 1)(n + 4)$.

$(n-1)(n+4)$

$n^2 - 1n + 4n - 4$

$(n+1)(n^2 + 3n - 4)$

$n^3 + 3n^2 - 4n + n^2 + 3n - 4$
$n^3 + 4n^2 - n - 4$

...... $n^3 + 4n^2 - n - 4$ ......

[3]

(b) n is a positive integer.
Prove that the value of $n(n + 3)(n + 1) - (n + 1)(n - 1)(n + 4)$ is a multiple of 4.

$n(n+3)(n+1)$ $(n^3 + 4n^2 - n - 4$

$(n^2 + 3n)(n+1)$

$n^3 + n^2 + 3n^2 + 3n$

$(n^3 + 4n^2 + 3n) - (n^3 + 4n^2 - n - 4)$

$4n + 4$ ...... $4(n+1)$ ......

$4(n+1)$

[3]

[Total 6 marks]

24 The diagram shows a quadratic graph.

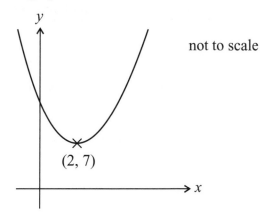

not to scale

The equation of the graph can be written in the form $y = (x - a)^2 + b$
The turning point of the quadratic has coordinates (2, 7).
A point on the graph has coordinates $(k, 128)$

Calculate the two possible values of k.

k = ... or k = ...

[Total 4 marks]

[TOTAL FOR PAPER = 80 MARKS]

12

Candidate Surname			Candidate Forename(s)	

Centre Number	Candidate Number	Candidate Signature

GCSE

Mathematics
Paper 2 (Calculator)

Higher Tier

Practice Paper
Time allowed: 1 hour 30 minutes

You must have:
Pen, pencil, eraser, ruler, protractor, pair of compasses.
You may use tracing paper.

You may use a calculator.

Instructions to candidates
- Use **black** ink to write your answers.
- Write your name and other details in the spaces provided above.
- Answer **all** questions in the spaces provided.
- In calculations show clearly how you worked out your answers.
- Do all rough work on the paper.
- Unless a question tells you otherwise, take the value of π to be 3.142, or use the π button on your calculator.

Information for candidates
- The marks available are given in brackets at the end of each question.
- You may get marks for method, even if your answer is incorrect.
- There are 22 questions in this paper. There are no blank pages.
- There are 80 marks available for this paper.

Answer ALL the questions.

Write your answers in the spaces provided.

You must show all of your working.

1   The length of a leaf is 11 cm to the nearest centimetre.

Put a ring around the upper bound for the length of the leaf.

11 cm   11.4 cm   (11.5 cm)   12 cm

[Total 1 mark]

2   The diagram shows a right-angled triangle.

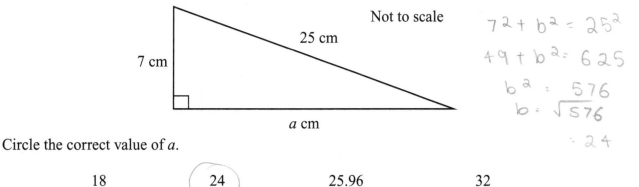

Circle the correct value of *a*.

18   (24)   25.96   32

[Total 1 mark]

3   Farah's teacher asks her to draw a quadrilateral with these three properties:

  • one line of symmetry
  • exactly two sides that are equal in length
  • two pairs of equal angles

Farah says, "There is no quadrilateral which has all these properties."

Draw a shape on the grid to show that Farah is wrong.

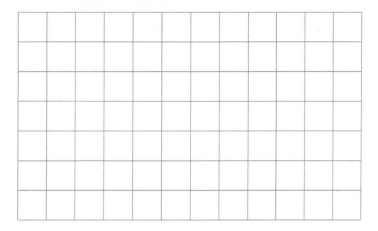

[Total 2 marks]

1

4 Calculate the value of $\dfrac{18.4 \times 2.56}{\sqrt{21.6 - 4 \times 1.55}}$. Give your answer correct to 3 significant figures.

12.00321

..........12.0..........

[Total 2 marks]

---

5 A drawer contains ties that are coloured either red or green or white or black.
George picks a tie at random from the drawer. The table shows some of the probabilities.

Colour of tie	Red	Green	White	Black
Probability	0.35	0.20		

The drawer contains exactly twice as many black ties as white ties.

George says, "Half the ties are coloured either red or white."
Is George correct? Tick a box.

Yes ☐ No ☐

Show how you worked out your answer.

[Total 3 marks]

---

6 Ollie and Amie each have an expression.

Ollie
$(x + 4)^2 - 1$

Amie
$(x + 5)(x + 3)$

Show clearly that Ollie's expression is equivalent to Amie's expression.

$(x+4)^2 - 1$
$(x+4)(x+4) - 1$
$x^2 + 8x + 16 - 1$
$x^2 + 8x + 15$

$(x+5)(x+3)$
$x^2 + 8x + 15$

$=$

[Total 3 marks]

7   The scatter graph shows the maximum power (in kW)
     and the maximum speed (in km/h) of a sample of cars.

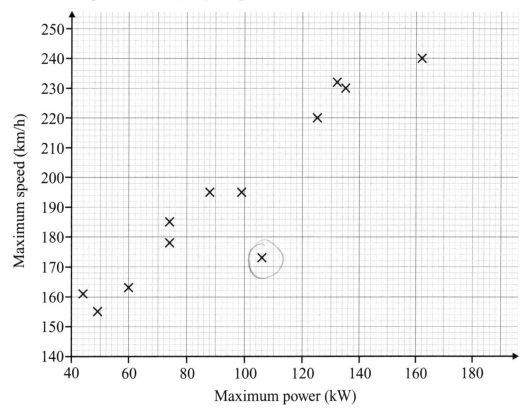

(a) One of the cars has a maximum speed of 220 km/h.
     Write down the maximum power of this car.

.... kW
[1]

(b) One of the points is an outlier as it does not fit in with the trend.
     Draw a ring around this point on the graph.

[1]

(c) Ignoring the outlier, describe the correlation shown on the scatter graph.

.... positive .... correlation
[1]

(d) A different car has a maximum power of 104 kW.
     By drawing a suitable line on your scatter graph, estimate the maximum speed of this car.

.... km/h
[2]

(e) Explain why it may not be reliable to use the scatter graph to estimate
     the maximum speed of a car with a maximum power of 190 kW.

....

....
[1]

[Total 6 marks]

3

Practice Paper 2

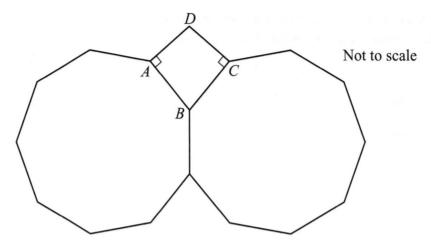

Not to scale

AB and *BC* are sides of congruent nine-sided regular polygons.
Angle *DAB* = angle *DCB* = 90°.

Calculate the size of angle *ADC*.

.... °

[Total 3 marks]

9   The functions f(x) and g(x) are shown below.

f(x) = $2x - 15$ g(x) = $x^2 + c$, where c is a constant.

(a)   Find f(–6)

$2(-6) - 15$

$-12 - 15 = -27$

.... -27 ....

[1]

(b)   Solve f(a) = 5

....

[1]

fg(4) = 25

(c)   Use this to find the value of *c*.

....

[2]

[Total 4 marks]

4

10 Orange juice and lemonade are mixed in the ratio 3 : 5 to make orangeade.

Orange juice costs £1.60 per litre.
Lemonade costs £1.20 per litre.

What is the cost of making 18 litres of orangeade?

£ ....

[Total 4 marks]

11 The diagram shows a solid aluminium cylinder and a solid silver cube.

Cylinder (aluminium)　　　　　Cube (silver)

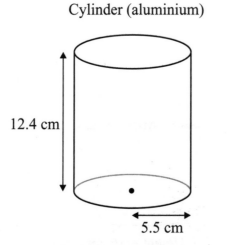
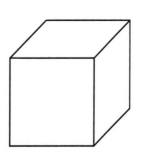

Not to scale

12.4 cm

5.5 cm

The cylinder and the cube have the same mass.
The density of aluminium is 2.7 g/cm³ and the density of silver is 10.5 g/cm³.

Calculate the side length of the cube. Give your answer correct to two significant figures.

.... cm

[Total 5 marks]

5

Practice Paper 2

12 Describe fully the single transformation equivalent to

- a reflection in the line $y = x$, followed by
- a reflection in the line $y = 0$.

Use the grid to help you.

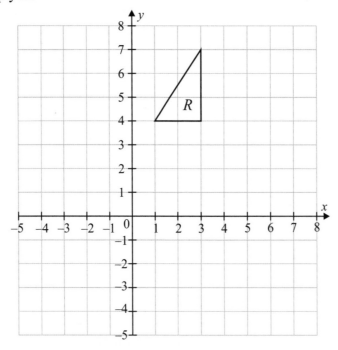

....

....

[Total 3 marks]

13 Isabel has two plant pots that are mathematically similar.

Not to scale

Height = 10 cm
Capacity = 250 ml

Height = 16 cm

Will the large plant pot hold one litre of compost? Tick a box.

Yes ☐   No ☐

Show how you worked out your answer.

[Total 3 marks]

6

14 *A*, *B* and *C* are points on the circumference of a circle with centre *O*.

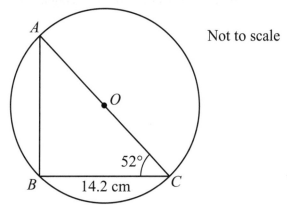

Not to scale

$BC = 14.2$ cm and angle $ACB = 52°$.

Calculate the circumference of the circle. Give your answer to 3 significant figures.

.... cm

[Total 4 marks]

15 A funfair stall runs a game played using this spinner. The rules of the game are shown below.

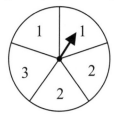

> **50p a go**
> Spin the spinner twice.
> Win £2 if your total
> score is 5 or more.

(a) Estimate the profit that the stall will make if the game is played 200 times.
Show how you worked out your answer.

£ ....

[5]

(b) Write down one assumption that you made about the spinner when you answered part (a).

....

....

[1]

[Total 6 marks]

16 Show, using algebra, that the recurring decimal $0.34\dot{7}$ is equal to the fraction $\frac{313}{900}$.

[Total 2 marks]

17 (a) Bayonie has £6000, which he wants to invest for three years.
He is choosing between two savings accounts which each pay compound interest.

> **Account 1**
> 2.5% per annum
> Fixed for 3 years

> **Account 2**
> Year 1: Interest rate 1.0%
> Year 2: Interest rate 1.5%
> Year 3: Interest rate 5.0%

Which account should he choose if he wants to receive the greatest possible amount of interest? Show how you worked out your answer.

....

[4]

(b) Sally invests a sum of money in an account for two years.
The account pays 2% per annum compound interest.
She receives a total of £606 interest.

Work out the amount of money she invested initially.

£ ....

[3]

[Total 7 marks]

18 Work out the values of a and b so that

$$\frac{ax + b}{2x^2 - 32} \times (x^2 - 2x - 8) = 3x + 6$$

$a = $ ....

$b = $ ....

[Total 4 marks]

19 (a) Show that the equation $x^3 - 5x + 2 = 0$ has a solution in the interval $0 < x < 0.5$.

[2]

(b) Show that $x^3 - 5x + 2 = 0$ can be written as $x = \dfrac{x^3 + 2}{5}$.

[1]

The iteration formula $x_{n+1} = \dfrac{x_n^3 + 2}{5}$ can be used with starting value $x_0 = 0$
to find the solution to $x^3 - 5x + 2 = 0$ which lies in the interval $0 < x < 0.5$.

(c) Find this solution correct to 4 decimal places.

....

[3]

[Total 6 marks]

134

20 For each part, work out a possible equation of the curve shown by the solid line.
The curve shown by a dotted line on each grid is $y = \cos x$.

(a)

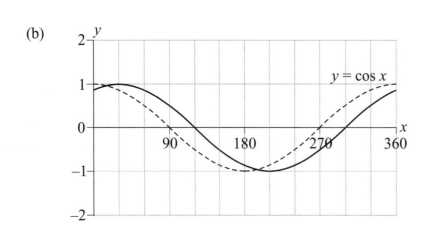

$y =$ ....
[1]

(b)

$y =$ ....
[1]

(c)

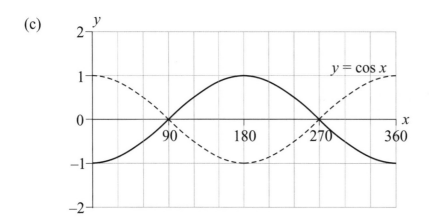

$y =$ ....
[1]

[Total 3 marks]

10

21 *OABC* is a parallelogram.

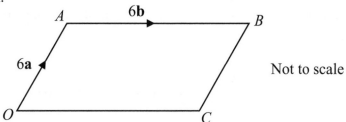

Not to scale

(a) Find the vector $\overrightarrow{AC}$.

....

[1]

When *OC* is extended, *D* is a point such that *OD* is twice *OC*.
M is the point with position vector $\overrightarrow{OM}$ = 4**a**.
N is the point on *BD* such that *BN* : *ND* = 1 : 2.

(b) Prove that *MN* is parallel to *AB*.

....

[3]

[Total 4 marks]

22 A curve has equation $x^2 + y^2 = 10$. The point $P(3, 1)$ is a point on the curve.

Work out the equation of the tangent to the curve at *P*.

....

[Total 4 marks]

[TOTAL FOR PAPER = 80 MARKS]

Practice Paper 2

Candidate Surname		Candidate Forename(s)	

Centre Number	Candidate Number	Candidate Signature

GCSE

Mathematics
Paper 3 (Calculator)

Higher Tier

Practice Paper
Time allowed: 1 hour 30 minutes

You must have:
Pen, pencil, eraser, ruler, protractor, pair of compasses.
You may use tracing paper.

You may use a calculator.

Instructions to candidates
- Use **black** ink to write your answers.
- Write your name and other details in the spaces provided above.
- Answer **all** questions in the spaces provided.
- In calculations show clearly how you worked out your answers.
- Do all rough work on the paper.
- Unless a question tells you otherwise, take the value of π to be 3.142, or use the π button on your calculator.

Information for candidates
- The marks available are given in brackets at the end of each question.
- You may get marks for method, even if your answer is incorrect.
- There are 23 questions in this paper. There are no blank pages.
- There are 80 marks available for this paper.

Answer ALL the questions.

Write your answers in the spaces provided.

You must show all of your working.

1 A function is represented by this number machine.

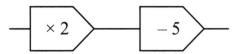

The output of the machine is 17. Circle the input.

7   11   14.5   29

[Total 1 mark]

---

2 Phil and Samira each throw an ordinary six-sided dice once.

Circle the probability that they both throw a number greater than 4.

$\frac{1}{9}$ $\frac{1}{4}$ $\frac{1}{3}$ $\frac{2}{3}$

[Total 1 mark]

---

3 Which of the numbers below is closest to $\frac{7}{9}$? Circle the correct answer.

0.77   0.7778   0.7   0.78   0.778

[Total 1 mark]

---

4 Natalie thinks of a whole number between 10 and 30.
Her number is not a prime number and when she squares her number, the final digit is 1.

What number did Natalie think of?

....

[Total 2 marks]

---

5 Ben has four number cards.

7   12   ?   ?

His four numbers have a median value of 12 and a mean of 13.
Work out the range of Ben's four numbers. Show how you worked out your answer.

....

[Total 3 marks]

1

Practice Paper 3

6 The diagram shows an object made from 8 centimetre cubes.

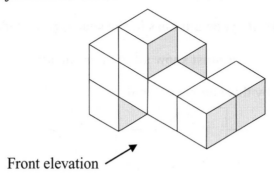

Front elevation

Draw on the grid below the plan view and the front elevation of the object.

Plan view

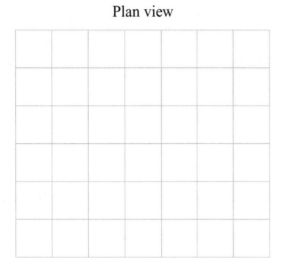

Front elevation

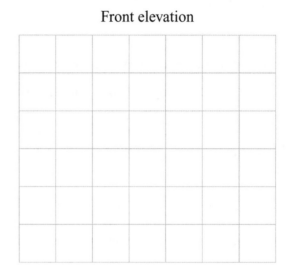

[Total 2 marks]

7 Anna and Carl both think of a sequence of numbers.

Anna's sequence

4th term = 17

Term-to-term rule is:
Add 3

Carl's sequence

Term-to-term rule is:
Add 6

The 1st term of Anna's sequence is twice the 1st term of Carl's sequence.

Work out the 5th term of Carl's sequence.

....

[Total 3 marks]

2

8 Here are the equations of five straight lines.

$$y = 2 \qquad 2y = x \qquad y = 2x + 1 \qquad y - 2x = -3 \qquad 3y = 2x + 2$$

Write each of the equations in the correct position in this table.
The first equation has been put in for you.

	Gradient equal to 2	Gradient not equal to 2
Passes though the point (2, 1)		
Does not pass though the point (2, 1)		$y = 2$

[Total 2 marks]

9 A chocolate manufacturer makes boxes of chocolates in three different sizes.

Box A   Box B   Box C

Box A contains c chocolates.
Box B contains 4 more chocolates than Box A.
Box C contains twice as many chocolates as Box B.
Altogether there are 60 chocolates.

Work out how many chocolates there are in each box.

Box A: ....

Box B: ....

Box C: ....

[Total 5 marks]

3

10   Two congruent trapeziums and two triangles fit inside a square of side 12 cm as shown.

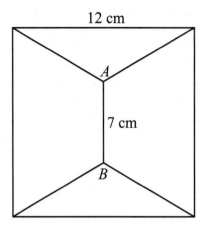

12 cm

A

7 cm

B

Not to scale

AB = 7 cm

Work out the area of each trapezium.

.... cm²

[Total 2 marks]

---

11   A route between Guilford and Bath has a distance of 180 kilometres.
     Dave drives from Guilford to Bath. He takes 3 hours.

     Olivia drives the same route. Her average speed is 15 kilometres per hour faster than Dave's.

     (a)   How long does it take Olivia to drive from Guilford to Bath?
           Give your answer in hours and minutes

.... hours .... minutes

[3]

     (b)   Why is it important to your calculation that Olivia drives the same route as Dave?

     ....

     ....

     ....

[1]

[Total 4 marks]

12 A bank interviews a sample of 500 of its customers to find out whether they are satisfied with the service the bank provides. The bank has both savings and mortgage customers.

The frequency tree summarises the responses.

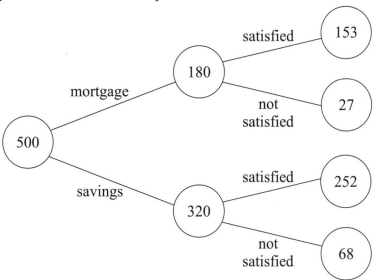

Comment on how satisfied the savings customers are in comparison with the mortgage customers. Give calculations to support your answer.

....

....

....

....

....

....

....

[Total 3 marks]

13 Simplify

(a) $(a^4)^3$

....

[1]

(b) a^0

....

[1]

(c) $3a^2b \times 2a^3b^2$

....

[2]

[Total 4 marks]

14 The ratio of angles in a triangle is $2:3:5$.
Show that this a right-angled triangle.

[Total 3 marks]

15 x and y satisfy these inequalities.

$$x \geq 1 \qquad y \geq \frac{x}{2} \qquad x + 2y \leq 8$$

(a) Show the region on the grid which satisfies these inequalities.

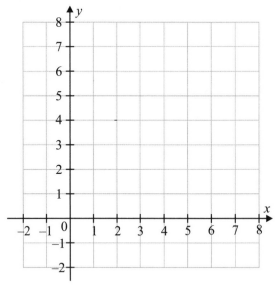

[4]

(b) How many different pairs of integer solutions satisfy all three inequalities?
Explain your answer.

....

....

....

[2]

[Total 6 marks]

16 *AB* and *BC* are perpendicular lines.

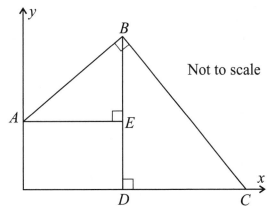

B has coordinates (12, 18).
C has coordinates (27, 0).
A is a point on the *y*-axis.

(a) Explain why triangles *AEB* and *BDC* are similar.

....

....

....

[2]

(b) Write the ratio *AE* : *BD* in its simplest form.

.... : ....

[2]

(c) Work out the coordinates of *E*.

(............. , ...)

[3]

[Total 7 marks]

144

17 The table shows some information about the ages of the adult members of a gym.

Age, A years	18 < A ≤ 20	20 < A ≤ 25	25 < A ≤ 30	30 < A ≤ 40	40 < A ≤ 60	60 < A ≤ 70	70 < A ≤ 90
Frequency	18	35	40	45	50	75	40

The gym manager draws a histogram to show this information. It is incorrect.

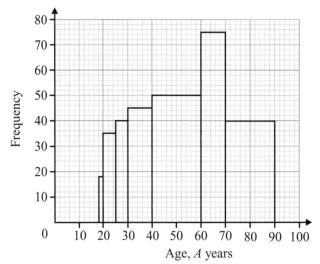

(a) Explain what error the manager has made when drawing the histogram.

....

....

[1]

(b) Draw the histogram correctly on the grid below.

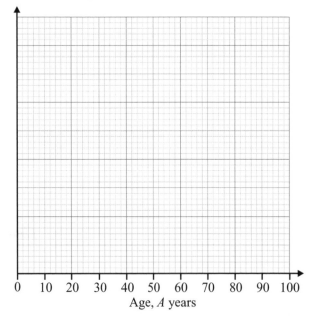

Age, A years

[3]

(c) The mean age of the adult members of the gym is 47 years.
    Explain why the mean does not give a very typical age for the members of this gym.

....

....

[1]

[Total 5 marks]

8

18 The grid shows a quadrilateral Q.

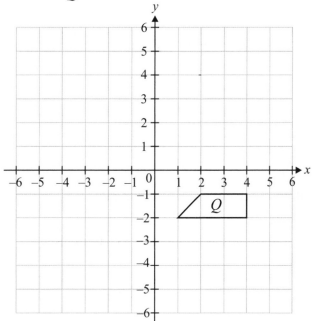

Draw the enlargement of Q using scale factor -2 and centre $(2, 0)$. Label the image R.

[Total 3 marks]

---

19 A museum has a collection of 200 thimbles.
The two-way table and the Venn diagram show some information about the thimbles.

	Made in Europe	Made outside Europe	Total
Antique			
Not antique			
Total		80	200

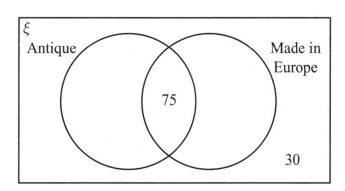

(a) Complete the table and the Venn diagram.

[3]

(b) Find the probability that a randomly chosen thimble is antique, given that it is made in Europe.

....

[2]

[Total 5 marks]

20 This cone is filled with water.

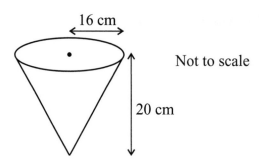

16 cm

Not to scale

20 cm

The radius of the cone is 16 cm to the nearest centimetre.
The height is 20 cm to the nearest centimetre.

Water leaks out of the bottom of the cone at a constant rate
of 0.39 litres per minute, to two significant figures.

Marion says, "The cone will definitely be empty after 15 minutes."
Is Marion correct? Tick a box.

Yes ☐   No ☐

Explain your answer.

[Total 5 marks]

21 The velocity-time graph on the right shows
the first two minutes of a car journey.

Calculate the distance the car travels
in the first two minutes of its journey.

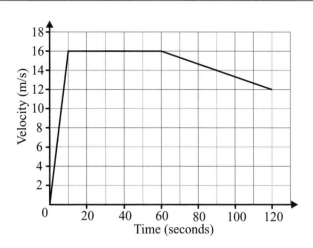

.... m

[Total 4 marks]

22 *ABC* is an isosceles triangle with *AB* = *AC* = 9 cm.
D is the point on *AC* such that *AD* = 5 cm and *BD* = 7 cm.

Calculate length *BC*.

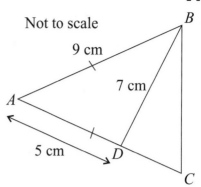

Not to scale

9 cm

7 cm

5 cm

.... cm

[Total 4 marks]

23 Hannah and Tim both think of a number.
Hannah's number is negative. Tim's number is one more than Hannah's.

They each take the reciprocal of their numbers. The sum of the reciprocals is $\frac{5}{6}$.

Use algebra to work out Hannah's original number.

....

[Total 5 marks]

[TOTAL FOR PAPER = 80 MARKS]

Practice Paper 3

Section One — Number

Page 3: Types of Number and BODMAS

1 $\dfrac{197.8}{\sqrt{0.01+0.23}} = \dfrac{197.8}{\sqrt{0.24}} = \dfrac{197.8}{0.489897948...}$
$= 403.757559... = 403.76$ (2 d.p.)
[2 marks available — 2 marks for answer correct to 2 decimal places, otherwise 1 mark for unrounded answer]

2 $\sqrt{\dfrac{12.71+137.936}{\cos 50° \times 13.2^2}} = \sqrt{\dfrac{150.646}{0.642787609... \times 174.24}}$
$= \sqrt{1.34506182...}$
$= 1.1597680...$
$= 1.16$ (2 d.p.)
[2 marks available — 2 marks for answer correct to 2 decimal places, otherwise 1 mark for unrounded answer]

3 E.g. $6 = \sqrt{3x+2y}$, so $36 = 3x + 2y$
Try different values of x and see what y-value each one gives:
$x = 2$: $3x = 6$, so $2y = 36 - 6 = 30$, so $y = 15$
$x = 4$: $3x = 12$, so $2y = 36 - 12 = 24$, so $y = 12$
[2 marks available — 1 mark for each correct pair of x and y values]
The only other possible solution is x = 6, y = 9 (you'll get full marks if you got this solution instead).

4 Irrational numbers: π, 0.6π, and $\sqrt{3}$.
[2 marks available — 2 marks for all three correct irrational numbers, lose 1 mark for one missing or a rational number included]
Don't be fooled — $\sqrt{16}$ = 4, which is rational.

Page 4: Multiples, Factors and Prime Factors

1 a) $2 \times 3 \times 5 \times 7$
      [2 marks available — 1 mark for correct method, 1 mark for all prime factors correct.]
   b) $3^2 \times 5^2 \times 7^2$
      [2 marks available — 1 mark for a correct method, 1 mark for all prime factors correct]

2 E.g. 4 (even) has three factors (1, 2 and 4).
   81 (odd) has five factors (1, 3, 9, 27 and 81).
   [2 marks available — 1 mark for each correct example of odd and even square numbers with a suitable number of factors.]
   These aren't the only square numbers that would work here — any pair where the odd number has more factors than the even number would get you the marks.

3 Common multiples of 6 and 7:
   42, 84, 126, 168, 210, 252, ... *[1 mark]*
   Factors of 252: 1, 2, 3, 4, 6, 7, 9, 12, 14, 18, 21, 28, 36, 42, 63, 84, 126, 252
   Factors of 420: 1, 2, 3, 4, 5, 6, 7, 10, 12, 14, 15, 20, 21, 28, 30, 35, 42, 60, 70, 84, 105, 140, 210, 420 *[1 mark for both sets of factors]*
   Common factors of 252 and 420:
   1, 2, 3, 4, 6, 7, 12, 14, 21, 28, 42, 84 *[1 mark]*
   So $x = 84$ *[1 mark]*
   [4 marks available in total — as above]

Page 5: LCM and HCF

1 a) LCM $= 3^7 \times 7^3 \times 11^2$ *[1 mark]*
   b) HCF $= 3^4 \times 11$ *[1 mark]*

2 a) LCM $= 2^8 \times 5^3 \times 7$
      [2 marks available — 2 marks for the correct answer, otherwise 1 mark for a common multiple of all three numbers]
   b) HCF $= 2^5$
      [2 marks available — 2 marks for the correct answer, otherwise 1 mark for a common factor of all three numbers]

3 Prime factorisation of $A = A$
   Prime factorisation of $B = B$ (as A and B are prime)
   So LCM $= A \times B$ (or AB)
   [2 marks available — 2 marks for the correct answer, otherwise 1 mark for stating that the prime factorisations of A and B are A and B]

Pages 6-7: Fractions

1 $\dfrac{5}{6} = \dfrac{100}{120}$ $\dfrac{3}{4} = \dfrac{90}{120}$ $\dfrac{7}{8} = \dfrac{105}{120}$ $\dfrac{4}{5} = \dfrac{96}{120}$
   All these fractions are less than one, and the largest is $\dfrac{105}{120}$,
   so the fraction closest to 1 is $\dfrac{7}{8}$ *[1 mark]*

2 a) $3\dfrac{1}{2} + 2\dfrac{3}{5} = \dfrac{7}{2} + \dfrac{13}{5} = \dfrac{35}{10} + \dfrac{26}{10} = \dfrac{35+26}{10} = \dfrac{61}{10}$ or $6\dfrac{1}{10}$
      [3 marks available — 1 mark for writing as improper fractions, 1 mark for writing over a common denominator, 1 mark for the correct answer]
   b) $3\dfrac{3}{4} - 2\dfrac{1}{3} = \dfrac{15}{4} - \dfrac{7}{3} = \dfrac{45}{12} - \dfrac{28}{12} = \dfrac{45-28}{12} = \dfrac{17}{12}$ or $1\dfrac{5}{12}$
      [3 marks available — 1 mark for writing as improper fractions, 1 mark for writing over a common denominator, 1 mark for the correct answer]
      If you've used a different method in Q2, but still shown your working, and ended up with the same final answer, then you still get full marks.

3 $1 - \dfrac{2}{15} - \dfrac{5}{12} = 1 - \dfrac{8}{60} - \dfrac{25}{60} = \dfrac{27}{60} = \dfrac{9}{20}$
   [3 marks available — 1 mark for writing over a common denominator, 1 mark for doing the subtraction correctly and 1 mark for simplifying to find the correct answer]

4 $\dfrac{2}{5} + \left(1 - \dfrac{6}{7}\right) = \dfrac{2}{5} + \dfrac{1}{7} = \dfrac{14}{35} + \dfrac{5}{35} = \dfrac{19}{35}$
   [3 marks available — 1 mark for finding the unshaded region of shape Y, 1 mark for writing over a common denominator and 1 mark for the correct answer]

5 $a = \dfrac{3}{4}, b = \dfrac{5}{2}$, so $\dfrac{1}{a} + \dfrac{1}{b} = \dfrac{4}{3} + \dfrac{2}{5} = \dfrac{20}{15} + \dfrac{6}{15} = \dfrac{26}{15}$ or $1\dfrac{11}{15}$
   [3 marks available — 1 mark for reciprocal fractions, 1 mark for rewriting over a common denominator, 1 mark for the correct answer]

6 a) $1\dfrac{2}{3} \times \dfrac{9}{10} = \dfrac{5}{3} \times \dfrac{9}{10} = \dfrac{45}{30} = \dfrac{3}{2} = 1\dfrac{1}{2}$
      [3 marks available — 1 mark for multiplying the two fractions together, 1 mark for an equivalent fraction, 1 mark for the correct final answer]
   b) $3\dfrac{1}{2} \div 1\dfrac{2}{5} = \dfrac{7}{2} \div \dfrac{7}{5} = \dfrac{7}{2} \times \dfrac{5}{7} = \dfrac{35}{14} = \dfrac{5}{2} = 2\dfrac{1}{2}$
      [3 marks available — 1 mark for taking the reciprocal and multiplying the two fractions together, 1 mark for an equivalent fraction, 1 mark for the correct final answer]

7 a) $17\dfrac{1}{2} \times \dfrac{1}{5} = \dfrac{35}{2} \times \dfrac{1}{5} = \dfrac{35}{10} = \dfrac{7}{2}$ *[1 mark]* tonnes of flour used to make cheese scones.
      Then $\dfrac{7}{2}$ out of 25 $= \dfrac{7}{2} \div 25 = \dfrac{7}{50}$ *[1 mark]*.
      [2 marks available in total — as above]
   b) $\dfrac{7}{50} = \dfrac{14}{100} = 14\%$ *[1 mark]*

Page 8: Fractions and Recurring Decimals

1 $10 \div 11 = 0.9\dot{0}$ *[1 mark]*

2 Convert to an equivalent fraction with all nines on the bottom
   $\dfrac{7}{33} = \dfrac{21}{99}$ *[1 mark]*
   Then the number on the top tells you the recurring part,
   so $\dfrac{7}{33} = 0.\dot{2}\dot{1}$ *[1 mark]*
   [2 marks available in total — as above]
   The first mark could also be obtained by using a division method.

3 a) Let $r = 0.\dot{7}$, so $10r = 7.\dot{7}$ *[1 mark]*

$10r - r = 7.\dot{7} - 0.\dot{7}$

$9r = 7$

$r = \frac{7}{9}$ *[1 mark]*

[2 marks available in total — as above]

b) Let $r = 0.\dot{2}\dot{6}$, so $100r = 26.\dot{2}\dot{6}$ *[1 mark]*

$100r - r = 26.\dot{2}\dot{6} - 0.\dot{2}\dot{6}$

$99r = 26$

$r = \frac{26}{99}$ *[1 mark]*

[2 marks available in total — as above]

c) Let $r = 1.3\dot{6}$, so $100r = 136.\dot{3}\dot{6}$ *[1 mark]*

$100r - r = 136.\dot{3}\dot{6} - 1.\dot{3}\dot{6}$

$99r = 135$ *[1 mark]*

$r = \frac{135}{99}$

$r = \frac{15}{11}$ or $1\frac{4}{11}$ *[1 mark]*

[3 marks available in total — as above]

4 Let $10r = 5.9\dot{0}$, so $1000r = 590.9\dot{0}$ *[1 mark]*

$990r = 585$ *[1 mark]*

$r = \frac{585}{990} = \frac{13}{22}$ *[1 mark]*

[3 marks available in total — as above]

Page 9: Rounding Numbers and Estimating

1 a) $\frac{215.7 \times 44.8}{460} \approx \frac{200 \times 40}{500} = \frac{8000}{500} = 16$

[3 marks available — 1 mark for correctly rounding 1 number to 1 significant figure, 1 mark for correctly rounding the other 2 numbers to 1 significant figure, 1 mark for correct answer]

b) The answer to a) will be smaller than the exact answer, because in the rounded fraction the numerator is smaller and denominator is larger compared to the exact calculation.

[2 marks available — 1 mark for 'smaller than the exact answer', 1 mark for correct reasoning]

2 $\sqrt{\frac{2321}{19.673 \times 3.81}} \approx \sqrt{\frac{2000}{20 \times 4}}$

[1 mark for rounding sensibly.]

$= \sqrt{\frac{100}{4}} = \sqrt{25}$ *[1 mark for either expression]*

$= 5$ *[1 mark]*

[3 marks available in total — as above]

You might have a different answer if you've rounded differently — as long as your rounding is sensible, you'll get the marks.

3 a) $V = \frac{1}{3}\pi(10)^2 \times 24 \approx \frac{1}{3} \times 3 \times 10^2 \times 20 = 100 \times 20 = 2000$ cm³

[2 marks available — 1 mark for rounding numbers sensibly, 1 mark for a suitable answer using rounded numbers]

b) Surface area $= (\pi \times 10 \times 26) + (2 \times \pi \times 10^2)$

$\approx (3 \times 10 \times 30) + (2 \times 3 \times 10^2) = (30 \times 30) + (6 \times 100)$

$= 900 + 600 = 1500$ cm²

[2 marks available — 1 mark for rounding numbers sensibly, 1 mark for a suitable answer using rounded numbers]

Pages 10-11: Bounds

1 a) 54.05 cm *[1 mark]*

b) lower bound for the width of the paper = 23.55 cm *[1 mark]*

lower bound for the perimeter

$= (54.05 \text{ cm} \times 2) + (23.55 \text{ cm} \times 2) = 155.2$ cm *[1 mark]*

[2 marks available in total — as above]

2 upper bound for x = 57.5 mm *[1 mark]*

upper bound for y = 32.5 mm *[1 mark]*

upper bound for area = 57.5 mm × 32.5 mm = 1868.75 mm²

$= 1870$ mm² to 3 s.f. *[1 mark]*

[3 marks available in total — as above]

3 Upper bound of x = 2.25 *[1 mark]*

So upper bound of $4x + 3 = 4 \times 2.25 + 3 = 12$

Lower bound of x = 2.15 *[1 mark]*

So lower bound of $4x + 3 = 4 \times 2.15 + 3 = 11.6$

Written as an interval, this is $11.6 \leq 4x + 3 < 12$

[2 marks — 1 for both bounds correct, 1 mark for expressing as an inequality correctly]

[4 marks available in total — as above]

4 Lower bound of difference = 13.65 − 8.35 *[1 mark]*

$= 5.3$ litres *[1 mark]*

[2 marks available in total — as above]

5 Upper bound of area = 5.25 cm² *[1 mark]*

Lower bound of height = 3.15 cm *[1 mark]*

$2 \times (5.25 \div 3.15) = 3.33$ to 2 d.p. *[1 mark]*

[3 marks available — as above]

6 lower bound for distance = 99.5 m

upper bound for time = 12.55 s *[1 mark for both]*

lower bound for speed $= \frac{99.5}{12.55}$ m/s = 7.928... m/s *[1 mark]*

lower bound for speed to 2 s.f. = 7.9 m/s

lower bound for speed to 1 s.f. = 8 m/s

upper bound for distance = 100.5 m

lower bound for time = 12.45 s *[1 mark for both]*

upper bound for speed $= \frac{100.5}{12.45}$ m/s = 8.072... m/s *[1 mark]*

upper bound for speed to 2 s.f. = 8.1 m/s

upper bound for speed to 1 s.f. = 8 m/s

The lower bound to 2 s.f. does not equal the upper bound to 2 s.f., but the lower bound to 1 s.f. does equal the upper bound to 1 s.f. So Dan's speed is 8 m/s to 1 significant figure.

[1 mark for comparing bounds to reach correct answer to 1 s.f.]

[5 marks available in total — as above]

7 lower bound for volume = $0.935 \times 0.605 \times 0.205 = 0.11596...$ m³

upper bound for volume = $0.945 \times 0.615 \times 0.215 = 0.12495...$ m³

Both the upper bound and lower bound round to 0.12 m³ to 2 d.p. (or 2 s.f.) so the volume to 2 d.p. is 0.12 m³.

[4 marks available — 1 mark for the correct upper and lower bounds for the dimensions, 1 mark for the correct lower bound for volume, 1 mark for the correct upper bound for volume, 1 mark for rounding to a suitable number of decimal places (or significant figures) to obtain the final answer]

Pages 12-13: Standard Form

1 a) $A = 4.834 \times 10^9 = 4\ 834\ 000\ 000$ *[1 mark]*

b) $B \times C = (2.7 \times 10^5) \times (5.8 \times 10^3) = (2.7 \times 5.8) \times (10^5 \times 10^3)$

$= 15.66 \times 10^8$ *[1 mark]*

$= 1.566 \times 10^9$ *[1 mark]*

[2 marks available in total — as above]

c) C, B, A (5.8×10^3, 2.7×10^5, 4.834×10^9) *[1 mark]*

2 time (s) = distance (miles) ÷ speed (miles/s)

$= (9.3 \times 10^7) \div (1.86 \times 10^5)$ seconds *[1 mark]*

$= 5 \times 10^2$ seconds *[1 mark]*

[2 marks available in total — as above]

3 $A = (5 \times 10^5) + (5 \times 10^3) + (5 \times 10^2) + (5 \times 10^{-2})$

$= 500\ 000 + 5000 + 500 + 0.05$ *[1 mark]*

$= 505\ 500.05$ *[1 mark]*

[2 marks available in total — as above]

4 $(4.5 \times 10^9) \div (1.5 \times 10^8) = (4.5 \div 1.5) \times (10^9 \div 10^8)$ *[1 mark]*

$= 3 \times 10^1 = 30$ *[1 mark]*. So the ratio is 1 : 30 *[1 mark]*

[3 marks available in total — as above]

5 a) number of tablets = dose (grams) ÷ dose per tablet (grams)

$= (4 \times 10^{-4}) \div (8 \times 10^{-5})$ *[1 mark]*

$= (4 \div 8) \times (10^{-4} \div 10^{-5})$

$= 0.5 \times 10^1$ *[1 mark]*

$= 5$ *[1 mark]*

[3 marks available in total — as above]

b) new dose = 4×10^{-4} grams + 6×10^{-5} grams *[1 mark]*
  = 4×10^{-4} grams + 0.6×10^{-4} grams *[1 mark]*
  = $(4 + 0.6) \times 10^{-4}$ grams
  = 4.6×10^{-4} grams per day *[1 mark]*
  [3 marks available in total — as above]
  You could have done this one by turning 4×10^{-4} into 40×10^{-5} and adding it to 6×10^{-5} instead.

6 Total weight of ship and passengers = $7.59 \times 10^7 + 2.1 \times 10^5$
  = 7.611×10^7 kg *[1 mark]*
  $(2.1 \times 10^5) \div (7.611 \times 10^7) = 0.002759...$ *[1 mark]*
  $0.002759 \times 100 = 0.28$ % (to 2 d.p.) *[1 mark]*
  [3 marks available in total — as above]

7 $\dfrac{3^2}{2^{122} \times 5^{120}} = \dfrac{9}{2^2(2^{120} \times 5^{120})} = \dfrac{9}{2^2 \times 10^{120}} = \dfrac{9}{4} \times \dfrac{1}{10^{120}} = 2.25 \times 10^{-120}$
  [2 marks available —1 mark for writing the denominator as a multiple of a power of 10, 1 mark for the correct answer]

Section Two — Algebra

Page 14: Algebra Basics

1 Area = $20 \times a \times b = 20ab$ cm^2 *[1 mark]*

2
  [1 mark]

3 Height = $7 \times (f + g) + 9 \times (h - g) + 5 \times 2h$ *[1 mark]*
  = $7f + 7g + 9h - 9g + 10h$
  = $7f - 2g + 19h$ cm *[1 mark]*
  [2 marks available in total — as above]

4 Perimeter of rectangle = $4x + 3 + 4x + 3 + 5x - 9 + 5x - 9$
  = $18x - 12$ cm *[1 mark]*.
  So perimeter of hexagon = $18x - 12$ cm.
  Hexagon side length = $(18x - 12) \div 6$ *[1 mark]*
  = $3x - 2$ cm *[1 mark]*.
  [3 marks available in total — as above]

Page 15: Powers and Roots

1 $5^{-2} = \dfrac{1}{5^2} = \dfrac{1}{25}$ *[1 mark]*

2 $8^{\frac{4}{3}} = (8^{\frac{1}{3}})^4 = (2)^4 = 16$
  [2 marks available — 1 mark for correct working, 1 mark for the correct final answer.]

3 $y^{-3} = \dfrac{1}{y^3}$, $y^1 = y$, $y^0 = 1$, $y^{\frac{1}{3}} = \sqrt[3]{y}$,
  so the correct order is... y^{-3} y^0 $y^{\frac{1}{3}}$ y^1 y^3
  [2 marks available — 2 marks for all 5 in the correct order, otherwise 1 mark for any 4 in the correct relative order.]
  If you can't identify which term is the smallest just by looking at them, try substituting a value for y into all the expressions and working out the answer. Then it'll be easy to tell which is the smallest.

4 a) $8^2 = 64$ and $9^2 = 81$, so $x = \sqrt{70} \approx 8.4$
    [2 marks available — 2 marks for 8.3, 8.4 or 8.5, otherwise 1 mark for any answer between 8 and 9 with 1 d.p.]
  b) $3^2 = 9$ and $3^3 = 27$, so $3^{2.7} \approx 20$, $y \approx 2.7$
    [2 marks available — 2 marks for 2.6, 2.7 or 2.8, otherwise 1 mark for any answer between 2 and 3 with 1 d.p.]

5 $(9a^4)^{\frac{1}{2}} = \sqrt{9a^4} = 3a^2$ *[1 mark]*
  $\dfrac{2ab^2}{6a^3b} = \dfrac{2}{6} \times \dfrac{a}{a^3} \times \dfrac{b^2}{b} = \dfrac{1}{3} \times \dfrac{1}{a^2} \times b = \dfrac{b}{3a^2}$ *[1 mark]*
  so $(9a^4)^{\frac{1}{2}} \times \dfrac{2ab^2}{6a^3b} = 3a^2 \times \dfrac{b}{3a^2} = b$ *[1 mark]*
  [3 marks available in total — as above]

Page 16: Multiplying Out Brackets

1 a) $5p(6 - 2p) = 30p - 10p^2$
    [2 marks available — 1 mark for each term]
  b) $(2t - 5)(3t + 4) = (2t \times 3t) + (2t \times 4) + (-5 \times 3t) + (-5 \times 4)$
    = $6t^2 + 8t - 15t - 20$ *[1 mark]*
    = $6t^2 - 7t - 20$ *[1 mark]*
    [2 marks available in total — as above]

2 $4(5x - 7) + 6(4 - 2x) = 20x - 28 + 24 - 12x$
  = $8x - 4 = 4(2x - 1)$
  So $a = 4$, $b = 2$ and $c = -1$
  [3 marks available — 1 mark for each correct value]

3 Area = $\frac{1}{2} \times$ base $\times$ height
  = $\frac{1}{2}(3x + 5y)(2x - 4y)$ *[1 mark]*
  = $\frac{1}{2} \times (6x^2 - 2xy - 20y^2)$ *[1 mark]*
  = $3x^2 - xy - 10y^2$ *[1 mark]*
  [3 marks available in total — as above]
  You could have instead multiplied $(2x - 4y)$ by $\frac{1}{2}$ first of all. The area would then just be $(3x + 5y)(x - 2y)$, which is a bit simpler to multiply out.

4 $(x - 1)(2x + 3)(2x - 3) = (x - 1)(4x^2 - 6x + 6x - 9)$
    = $(x - 1)(4x^2 - 9)$
    = $4x^3 - 4x^2 - 9x + 9$
  [3 marks available — 3 marks for the correct answer, otherwise 1 mark for correctly multiplying two sets of brackets together, 1 mark for attempting to multiply this product by the third set of brackets]
  The trick here is spotting that the second pair of brackets multiply out to give just two terms (a difference of two squares), which makes the second multiplication much easier.

Page 17: Factorising

1 a) $7y - 21y^2 = 7(y - 3y^2) = 7y(1 - 3y)$
    [2 marks available — 1 mark for each correct factor]
  b) $2v^3w + 8v^2w^2 = 2(v^3w + 4v^2w^2) = 2v^2w(v + 4w)$
    [2 marks available — 1 mark for each correct factor]

2 a) $x^2 - 16 = x^2 - 4^2 = (x + 4)(x - 4)$ *[1 mark]*
  b) $9n^2 - 4m^2 = (3n)^2 - (2m)^2 = (3n + 2m)(3n - 2m)$
    [2 marks available — 1 mark for each correct factor]
  c) $3y^2 - 15 = 3(y^2 - 5) = 3[y^2 - (\sqrt{5})^2] = 3(y + \sqrt{5})(y - \sqrt{5})$
    [2 marks available — 1 mark for each correct factor]

3 $x^3 - 25x = x(x^2 - 25) = x(x + 5)(x - 5)$
  [3 marks available — 1 mark for each correct factor]

Page 18: Manipulating Surds

1 $(2 + \sqrt{3})(5 - \sqrt{3}) = (2 \times 5) + (2 \times -\sqrt{3}) + (\sqrt{3} \times 5) + (\sqrt{3} \times -\sqrt{3})$
    = $10 - 2\sqrt{3} + 5\sqrt{3} - 3$
    = $7 + 3\sqrt{3}$
  [2 marks available — 1 mark for correct working, 1 mark for the correct answer]

2 $2\sqrt{50} = 2\sqrt{25 \times 2} = 2 \times 5\sqrt{2} = 10\sqrt{2}$
  $(\sqrt{2})^3 = \sqrt{2} \times \sqrt{2} \times \sqrt{2} = (\sqrt{2})^2 \times \sqrt{2} = 2\sqrt{2}$
  So $2\sqrt{50} - (\sqrt{2})^3 = 10\sqrt{2} - 2\sqrt{2} = 8\sqrt{2}$
  [2 marks available — 2 marks for the correct answer, otherwise 1 mark for correctly simplifying either surd]

3 $\sqrt{396} = \sqrt{36 \times 11} = 6\sqrt{11}$ *[1 mark]*
  $\dfrac{22}{\sqrt{11}} = \dfrac{22\sqrt{11}}{11} = 2\sqrt{11}$ *[1 mark]*
  $\sqrt{44} = \sqrt{4 \times 11} = 2\sqrt{11}$
  So $\dfrac{220}{\sqrt{44}} = \dfrac{220}{2\sqrt{11}} = \dfrac{220\sqrt{11}}{22} = 10\sqrt{11}$ *[1 mark]*
  So $\sqrt{396} + \dfrac{22}{\sqrt{11}} - \dfrac{220}{\sqrt{44}} = 6\sqrt{11} + 2\sqrt{11} - 10\sqrt{11} = -2\sqrt{11}$
  [1 mark]
  [4 marks available — as above]

4 $\dfrac{1+\sqrt{7}}{3-\sqrt{7}} = \dfrac{(1+\sqrt{7})(3+\sqrt{7})}{(3-\sqrt{7})(3+\sqrt{7})}$ *[1 mark]*

$= \dfrac{3+\sqrt{7}+3\sqrt{7}+7}{9-7}$ *[1 mark]*

$= \dfrac{10+4\sqrt{7}}{2}$ *[1 mark]*

$= 5+2\sqrt{7}$ *[1 mark]*

[4 marks available in total — as above]

Pages 19-20: Solving Equations

1 Let the number of tickets Felix sells be x.
Then Poppy sells $2x$ tickets and Alexi sells $(2x + 25)$ tickets,
so $x + 2x + (2x + 25) = 700$
$5x + 25 = 700$
$5x = 675$ and $x = 135$
So Felix sells 135 tickets, Poppy sells $2 \times 135 = 270$ tickets and
Alexi sells $(2 \times 135) + 25$ tickets = 295 tickets.
*[5 marks available — 1 mark for finding expressions for the
number of tickets each person sells, 1 mark for forming an
equation to solve, 1 mark for solving to find the number of tickets
Felix sells, 1 mark for the number of tickets Poppy sells,
1 mark for the number of tickets Alexi sells]*

2 $2x + 6 = 5(x - 3)$ *[1 mark]*
$2x + 6 = 5x - 15$
$21 = 3x$ *[1 mark]*
$x = 7$ cm *[1 mark]*
So one side of the triangle measures $2(7) + 6 = 20$ cm *[1 mark]*
[4 marks available in total — as above]

3 $\dfrac{5}{4}(2c - 1) = 3c - 2$
$5(2c - 1) = 4(3c - 2)$ *[1 mark]*
$(5 \times 2c) + (5 \times -1) = (4 \times 3c) + (4 \times -2)$
$10c - 5 = 12c - 8$
$12c - 10c = 8 - 5$ *[1 mark]*
$2c = 3$ so $c = \dfrac{3}{2}$ or 1.5 *[1 mark]*
[3 marks available in total — as above]

4 If Neil worked h hours, Liam worked $(h + 30)$ hours.
$360 \div 4.5 = 80$
$80 = h + (h + 30) = 2h + 30$
$50 = 2h$, so $h = 25$
Neil worked 25 hours and Liam worked $(25 + 30) = 55$ hours.
*[3 marks available — 1 mark for forming an equation for the
total number of hours, 1 mark for solving the equation to find h,
1 mark for finding the number of hours each boy worked]*

5 a) $5x^2 = 180$
$x^2 = 36$ *[1 mark]*
$x = \pm 6$ *[1 mark]*
[2 marks available in total — as above]

b) $\dfrac{8 - 2x}{3} + \dfrac{2x + 4}{9} = 12$
$\dfrac{9(8 - 2x)}{3} + \dfrac{9(2x + 4)}{9} = 9 \times 12$
$3(8 - 2x) + (2x + 4) = 108$
$24 - 6x + 2x + 4 = 108$
$6x - 2x = 24 + 4 - 108$
$4x = -80$ so $x = -20$
*[4 marks available — 2 marks for rearranging to remove the
fractions, 1 mark for rearranging to get all x-terms on one
side, 1 mark for correct answer]*

6 If one number is x, the other number is $3x$.
$3x^2 = 147$ *[1 mark]*, so $x^2 = 49$, which means that $x = 7$
(as $x > 0$) *[1 mark]* and $3x = 21$ *[1 mark]*,
so Hassan is thinking of 7 and 21.
[3 marks available in total — as above]

Pages 21-22: Formulas

1 a) $F = \dfrac{9}{5}C + 32$, so $\dfrac{9}{5}C = F - 32$ and $C = \dfrac{5}{9}(F - 32)$
*[2 marks available — 1 mark for subtracting 32 from
each side, 1 mark for the correct answer.]*

b) When $F = 41$, $C = \dfrac{5}{9}(41 - 32) = \dfrac{5}{9}(9) = 5$ °C
*[2 marks available — 1 mark for correct substitution,
1 mark for the correct answer.]*

2 a) $P = \dfrac{V^2}{R} = \dfrac{12^2}{16} = \dfrac{144}{16} = 9$ W *[1 mark]*

b) $P = \dfrac{V^2}{R}$, so $25 = \dfrac{20^2}{R}$ *[1 mark]*. $R = \dfrac{20^2}{25} = \dfrac{400}{25}$,
$= 16\ \Omega$ *[1 mark]*
[2 marks available in total — as above]

3 $s = \dfrac{1}{2}gt^2$, so $gt^2 = 2s$ *[1 mark]*, $t^2 = \dfrac{2s}{g}$ *[1 mark]*,
$t = \sqrt{\dfrac{2s}{g}}$ *[1 mark]*
[3 marks available in total — as above]

4 a) $a + y = \dfrac{b - y}{a}$, so...
$a(a + y) = b - y$ *[1 mark]*, $a^2 + ay = b - y$,
$ay + y = b - a^2$ *[1 mark]*, $y(a + 1) = b - a^2$ *[1 mark]*,
$y = \dfrac{b - a^2}{a + 1}$ *[1 mark]*
[4 marks available in total — as above]

b) When $a = 3$ and $b = 6$, $y = \dfrac{6 - 3^2}{3 + 1} = -\dfrac{3}{4}$ or -0.75 *[1 mark]*

5 $x = \sqrt{\dfrac{(1 + n)}{(1 - n)}}$, so $x^2 = \dfrac{(1 + n)}{(1 - n)}$ *[1 mark]*, $x^2(1 - n) = 1 + n$,
$x^2 - x^2 n = 1 + n$ *[1 mark]*, $x^2 - 1 = n + x^2 n$ *[1 mark]*,
$x^2 - 1 = n(1 + x^2)$ *[1 mark]*,
$n = \dfrac{x^2 - 1}{1 + x^2}$ *[1 mark]*
[5 marks available in total — as above]

6 Rearrange to make y the subject:
$x = \dfrac{1 - y}{x}$
$x^2 = 1 - y$
$y = 1 - x^2$
$x > 1$, so $x^2 > 1$. Then $1 - x^2 < 0$, so y is always negative.
*[3 marks available — 1 mark for rearranging the formula to
make y the subject, 1 mark for showing that $x^2 > 1$ or $1 - x^2 < 0$,
1 mark for stating that y is negative]*

7 $b = \sqrt{2a - 1}$ so $b^2 = 2a - 1$ and $b^4 = (2a - 1)^2 = 4a^2 - 4a + 1$
$c = 2b^4 + 4b^2 = 2(4a^2 - 4a + 1) + 4(2a - 1)$
$= 8a^2 - 8a + 2 + 8a - 4 = 8a^2 - 2$
Rearrange to make a the subject:
$c = 8a^2 - 2$
$a^2 = \dfrac{c + 2}{8}$
$a = \pm\sqrt{\dfrac{c + 2}{8}}$
*[4 marks available — 1 mark for writing b^2 and b^4 in terms of
a, 1 mark for writing c in terms of a, 1 mark for rearranging to
make a^2 the subject, 1 mark for the correct answer]*

Page 23: Factorising Quadratics

1 Let the two consecutive even numbers be $2n$ and $2n + 2$.
$2n(2n + 2) = 288$ *[1 mark]*
$4n^2 + 4n = 288$
$4n^2 + 4n - 288 = 0$
$n^2 + n - 72 = 0$
$(n + 9)(n - 8) = 0$ *[1 mark]*, so $n = -9$ or $n = 8$.
The numbers are positive, so $n = 8$ *[1 mark]*.
The larger of the two numbers is $2(8) + 2 = 18$ *[1 mark]*.
[4 marks available in total — as above]

2 a) $(5x - 9)(x - 2)$
*[2 marks available — 1 mark for correct numbers in brackets,
1 mark for correct signs]*

Answers

b) Replacing x with $(x-1)$ in the factorised expression from a)...
$5(x-1)^2 - 19(x-1) + 18 = (5(x-1) - 9)((x-1) - 2)$ *[1 mark]*
$= (5x - 5 - 9)(x - 1 - 2)$
$= (5x - 14)(x - 3)$ *[1 mark]*
[2 marks available in total — as above]

3 The area of the square is $(x+3)(x+3) = x^2 + 6x + 9$. *[1 mark]*
The area of the triangle is $\frac{1}{2}(2x+2)(x+3)$
$= \frac{1}{2}(2x^2 + 6x + 2x + 6) = \frac{1}{2}(2x^2 + 8x + 6)$
$= x^2 + 4x + 3$ *[1 mark]*
So the area of the whole shape is $x^2 + 6x + 9 + x^2 + 4x + 3$
$= 2x^2 + 10x + 12$ *[1 mark]*
$2x^2 + 10x + 12 = 60$, so $2x^2 + 10x - 48 = 0$ *[1 mark]*
So $x^2 + 5x - 24 = 0$
$(x-3)(x+8) = 0$ *[1 mark]*

$x - 3 = 0$ or $x + 8 = 0$
$x = 3$ or $x = -8$
[1 mark for both solutions]

A length can't have a negative value so the
answer must be $x = 3$ *[1 mark]*
[7 marks available in total — as above]

Page 24: The Quadratic Formula

1 $a = 1$, $b = 5$ and $c = 3$

$x = \dfrac{-5 \pm \sqrt{5^2 - 4 \times 1 \times 3}}{2 \times 1} = \dfrac{-5 \pm \sqrt{13}}{2}$

$x = -0.70$ or $x = -4.30$
[3 marks available — 1 mark for correct substitution,
1 mark for each correct solution]

2 $a = 2$, $b = -7$ and $c = 2$

$x = \dfrac{-(-7) \pm \sqrt{(-7)^2 - 4 \times 2 \times 2}}{2 \times 2} = \dfrac{7 \pm \sqrt{33}}{4}$

$x = 3.19$ or $x = 0.31$
[3 marks available — 1 mark for correct substitution,
1 mark for each correct solution]

3 $a = 3$, $b = -2$ and $c = -4$

$x = \dfrac{-(-2) \pm \sqrt{(-2)^2 - 4 \times 3 \times -4}}{2 \times 3} = \dfrac{2 \pm \sqrt{52}}{6} = \dfrac{2 \pm 2\sqrt{13}}{6}$

$x = \dfrac{1 + \sqrt{13}}{3}$ or $x = \dfrac{1 - \sqrt{13}}{3}$

[3 marks available — 1 mark for correct substitution, 1 mark for
each correct solution. Lose a mark if answers aren't simplified]

4 $(x+3)(3x+3) = 30$
$3x^2 + 12x + 9 = 30$
$3x^2 + 12x - 21 = 0$
$x^2 + 4x - 7 = 0$
$a = 1$, $b = 4$ and $c = -7$

$x = \dfrac{-4 \pm \sqrt{4^2 - 4 \times 1 \times -7}}{2 \times 1} = \dfrac{-4 \pm \sqrt{44}}{2}$

$= \dfrac{-4 \pm 2\sqrt{11}}{2} = -2 \pm \sqrt{11}$

Lengths cannot be negative, so $x = -2 + \sqrt{11}$.
So the longer side is $3(-2 + \sqrt{11}) + 3 = -3 + 3\sqrt{11}$ cm
[5 marks available — 1 mark for setting up the quadratic
equation, 1 mark for the correct substitution, 1 mark for solving
the quadratic equation, 1 mark for choosing the correct value
of x, 1 mark for the correct answer]

Page 25: Completing the Square

1 $(x+2)^2 - 9 = x^2 + 4x + 4 - 9$ *[1 mark]* $= x^2 + 4x - 5$
$a = 4$ and $b = -5$ *[1 mark]*
[2 marks available in total — as above]

2 a) $-10 \div 2 = -5$, so $p = -5$ and the bit in brackets is $(x-5)^2$.
[1 mark]
Expanding the brackets: $(x-5)^2 = x^2 - 10x + 25$. *[1 mark]*
To complete the square: $-5 - 25 = -30$, so $q = -30$. *[1 mark]*
$p = -5$ and $q = -30$
[3 marks available in total — as above]

b) $(x-5)^2 - 30 = 0$, so $(x-5)^2 = 30$ and $x - 5 = \pm\sqrt{30}$
So $x = 5 + \sqrt{30}$ or $x = 5 - \sqrt{30}$
[2 marks available — 1 mark for each correct solution]

3 a) $2(x^2 - 4x) + 19$
$4 \div 2 = 2$, so the first bit is $2[(x-2)^2]$
Expanding the brackets: $2(x^2 - 4x + 4) = 2x^2 - 8x + 8$
To complete the square: $19 - 8 = 11$
So $2x^2 - 8x + 19 = 2(x-2)^2 + 11$
[4 marks available — 1 mark for dividing the first two terms
by 2, 1 mark dividing the x-term by 2 to find the value of b,
1 mark for finding the value of c, 1 mark for the full correct
answer]

b) Minimum value = 11, which occurs at $x = 2$, so the coordinates
of the minimum point are $(2, 11)$ *[1 mark]*

c) This quadratic is u-shaped and its minimum value is 11, so it's
always greater than 0. This means it never crosses the x-axis.
[1 mark]

Page 26: Algebraic Fractions

1 $\dfrac{4x^2 + 10x - 6}{16x^2 - 4} = \dfrac{(4x-2)(x+3)}{(4x-2)(4x+2)} = \dfrac{x+3}{4x+2}$

[3 marks available — 1 mark for correctly factorising the
denominator, 1 mark for correctly factorising the numerator,
1 mark for the correct answer]

2 $\dfrac{2a-8}{a^2-9} \div \dfrac{a^2 - 2a - 8}{a^2 + 5a + 6} \times (2a^2 - a - 15)$

$= \dfrac{2a-8}{a^2-9} \times \dfrac{a^2 + 5a + 6}{a^2 - 2a - 8} \times (2a^2 - a - 15)$

$= \dfrac{2(a-4)}{(a+3)(a-3)} \times \dfrac{(a+3)(a+2)}{(a+2)(a-4)} \times (2a+5)(a-3)$

$= 2(2a+5)$ (or $4a + 10$)
[5 marks available — 1 mark for converting to a multiplication,
1 mark for factorising the first fraction, 1 mark for factorising the
second fraction, 1 mark for factorising the quadratic term, 1 mark
for cancelling to reach correct answer]

3 $\dfrac{2}{3} + \dfrac{m-2n}{m+3n} = \dfrac{2(m+3n)}{3(m+3n)} + \dfrac{3(m-2n)}{3(m+3n)} = \dfrac{2(m+3n) + 3(m-2n)}{3(m+3n)}$

$= \dfrac{2m + 6n + 3m - 6n}{3(m+3n)} = \dfrac{5m}{3(m+3n)}$

[3 marks available — 1 mark for finding the common
denominator, 1 mark for a correct method for addition,
1 mark for the correct final answer]

4 $\dfrac{1}{x-5} + \dfrac{2}{x-2} = \dfrac{x-2}{(x-5)(x-2)} + \dfrac{2(x-5)}{(x-5)(x-2)}$

$= \dfrac{(x-2) + 2(x-5)}{(x-5)(x-2)} = \dfrac{x - 2 + 2x - 10}{(x-5)(x-2)} = \dfrac{3x - 12}{(x-5)(x-2)}$

[3 marks available — 1 mark for finding the common
denominator, 1 mark for a correct method for addition,
1 mark for the correct final answer]

Pages 27-29: Sequences

1 a) Common difference = 5, so $5n$ is in the formula.
To get from $5n$ to each term, you have to subtract 2,
so the expression for the nth term is $5n - 2$.
[2 marks available — 2 marks for correct expression,
otherwise 1 mark for finding 5n.]

b) The nth term is $5n - 2$ and the $(n+1)$th term is
$5(n+1) - 2 = 5n + 5 - 2 = 5n + 3$
Product of the nth and $(n+1)$th terms:
$(5n-2)(5n+3) = 25n^2 + 15n - 10n - 6 = 25n^2 + 5n - 6$
[2 marks available — 1 mark for finding an expression for
the nth and (n + 1)th terms, 1 mark for multiplying to find
the correct product]

2 a) Common difference = 4 so $4n$ is in the formula.
To get from $4n$ to each term, you have to subtract 1,
so the expression for the nth term is $4n - 1$.
[2 marks available — 2 marks for correct expression,
otherwise 1 mark for finding 4n]

Answers

b) All multiples of 4 are even numbers, and an even number minus 1 is always an odd number. So all the terms in this sequence will be odd numbers. *[1 mark]*
502 is an even number, so 502 cannot be in the sequence. *[1 mark]*
[2 marks available in total — as above]

3 a) To get from one term to the next, you have to multiply by $\sqrt{2}$, so the next term is $4\sqrt{2}$ and the next one is $4\sqrt{2} \times \sqrt{2} = 8$.
[2 marks available — 1 mark for each correct term]

b) $(\sqrt{2})^n$ *[1 mark]*

4 a) $u_1 = 0.5$
$u_2 = 2(0.5) + 1 = 1 + 1 = 2$ *[1 mark]*
$u_3 = 2(2) + 1 = 4 + 1 = 5$ *[1 mark]*
[2 marks available in total — as above]

b) $u_1 = 1.5$
$u_2 = 2(1.5) + 1 = 3 + 1 = 4$ *[1 mark]*
$u_3 = 2(4) + 1 = 8 + 1 = 9$ *[1 mark]*
$u_4 = 2(9) + 1 = 18 + 1 = 19$ *[1 mark]*
[3 marks available in total — as above]

c) If $u_1 = -1$, all terms in the sequence are also -1 *[1 mark]*

5 a) The difference between the terms is 4, 6, 8, ... so to find the next term, add 10 onto 20: $20 + 10 = 30$.
[2 marks available — 2 marks for the correct answer, otherwise 1 mark for finding the differences between the terms]

b) Sequence: 2   6   12   20
First difference: 4   6   8
Second difference: 2   2 *[1 mark]*
Coefficient of $n^2 = 2 \div 2 = 1$.
Actual sequence $- n^2$ sequence:
      1   2   3   4
Difference: 1   1   1
So this is a linear sequence with nth term n *[1 mark]*.
So the nth term is $n^2 + n$ *[1 mark]*.
[3 marks available in total — as above]

6 a) $u_1 = 2$
$u_2 = \dfrac{-1}{2(2)} = -0.25$
$u_3 = \dfrac{-1}{2(-0.25)} = 2$
$u_4 = \dfrac{-1}{2(2)} = -0.25$
[2 marks available — 2 marks for all three values correct, otherwise 1 mark for one or two values correct]

b) $u_{50} = -0.25$ *[1 mark]*

7 a) Number of grey squares as a sequence: 1, 5, 9, 13, ...
Common difference = 4 so $4n$ is in the formula.
To get from $4n$ to each term, you have to subtract 3, so the expression for the nth term is $4n - 3$.
[2 marks available — 2 marks for correct expression, otherwise 1 mark for finding $4n$]

b) Assume Giles makes the nth and $(n + 1)$th patterns.
He uses $4n - 3$ grey squares in the nth pattern and $4(n + 1) - 3 = 4n + 4 - 3 = 4n + 1$ grey squares in the $(n + 1)$th pattern *[1 mark]*. He uses 414 grey squares in total, so
$(4n - 3) + (4n + 1) = 414$ *[1 mark]*
$8n - 2 = 414$
$8n = 416$
$n = 52$
So Giles has made the 52nd and 53rd patterns *[1 mark]*.
[3 marks available in total — as above]

c) Total number of squares:
      1   7   17   31
First difference: 6   10   14
Second difference: 4   4 *[1 mark]*
The second differences are constant so the sequence is quadratic. Coefficient of $n^2 = 4 \div 2 = 2$ *[1 mark]*.
Actual sequence $- 2n^2$ sequence:
      -1   -1   -1   -1
So the nth term of the sequence is $2n^2 - 1$ *[1 mark]*.
[3 marks available in total — as above]

Page 30: Inequalities

1 $-4 \le 2x < 8$ *[1 mark]*

2 $4x + 1 > x - 5$, so $3x > -6$ *[1 mark]* and $x > -2$ *[1 mark]*
[2 marks available in total — as above]

3 $5n - 3 \le 17$, so $5n \le 20$, so $n \le 4$ *[1 mark]*
$2n + 6 > 8$, so $2n > 2$, so $n > 1$ *[1 mark]*
Putting these together gives $1 < n \le 4$, so $n = \{2, 3, 4\}$ *[1 mark]*
[3 marks available in total — as above]
Don't forget to give your answer in set notation here.

4 $2n + (2n + 2) + (2n + 4) < 1000$ *[1 mark]*
$6n + 6 < 1000$
$n < 165.666...$ *[1 mark]*
So the largest possible values of the numbers are obtained when $n = 165$, which gives 330, 332 and 334 *[1 mark]*.
[3 marks available in total — as above]

5 a) $5x^2 < 80$, so $x^2 < 16$. The solutions of $x^2 = 16$ are $x = 4$ and $x = -4$, so $x^2 < 16$ when $-4 < x < 4$.
[3 marks available — 1 mark for finding the square roots of 16, 1 mark for $-4 < x$, 1 mark for $x < 4$]

b) $x^2 + 1 = x + 7$ rearranges to give $x^2 - x - 6 = 0$.
$x^2 - x - 6 = 0$ factorises to give $(x + 2)(x - 3) = 0$.
The graph of $y = x^2 - 6$ is a u-shaped quadratic that crosses the x-axis at $x = -2$ and $x = 3$:

The graph is below 0 when x is greater than -2 and less than 3. So $-2 < x < 3$.
[3 marks available — 1 mark for rearranging and factorising the quadratic to find the solutions, 1 mark for $-2 < x$, 1 mark for $x < 3$]

Page 31: Graphical Inequalities

1 a)

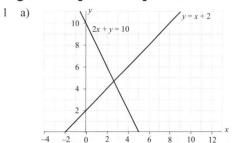

[2 marks available — 1 mark for correctly drawing $2x + y = 10$, 1 mark for correctly drawing $y = x + 2$]

b)

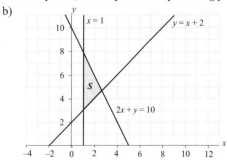

[2 marks available — 2 marks for correctly shaded area, lose 1 mark if the wrong side of one line is shaded]

Answers

2

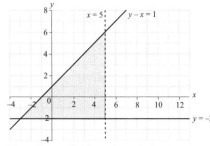

[4 marks available — 1 mark for drawing each line correctly, 1 mark for shading the correct area]

3   $y \geq 2$ *[1 mark]*, $x + y \leq 8$ *[1 mark]* and $y \leq x$ *[1 mark]*
[3 marks available in total — as above]

Pages 32-33: Iterative Methods

1

x	$x^3 - 4x + 2$	
-2	2	Positive
-3	-13	Negative
-2.1	1.139	Positive
-2.2	0.152	Positive
-2.3	-0.967	Negative
-2.21	0.046139	Positive
-2.22	-0.061048	Negative

The sign change shows that there's a solution between
$x = -2.22$ and $x = -2.21$, so $x = -2.2$ to 1 d.p.
[4 marks available — 1 mark for rows showing a sign change between $x = -2$ and $x = -3$, 1 mark for rows showing a sign change between $x = -2.2$ and $x = -2.3$, 1 mark for rows showing a sign change between $x = -2.21$ and $x = -2.22$, 1 mark for the correct value of x]

2   $x_0 = 1$ $x_1 = 0.888888...$
    $x_2 = 0.876881...$ $x_3 = 0.876750...$
    $x_4 = 0.876750...$
    $x_4 = x_3$ to 5 d.p. so $x = 0.87675$ to 5 d.p.

[3 marks available — 1 mark for carrying out the iteration correctly, 1 mark for stopping when the x-values are equal when rounded to 5 d.p., 1 mark for the correct value of x]

3   a)   Find the value of the expression at $x = 1.5$ and $x = 2$:
         $x = 1.5$: $3(1.5) - 2(1.5)^3 + 5 = 2.75$
         $x = 2$: $3(2) - 2(2)^3 + 5 = -5$

         There is a sign change between $x = 1.5$ and $x = 2$,
         so there is a solution in that interval.
         [2 marks available — 1 mark for finding the values when $x = 1.5$ and $x = 2$, 1 mark for stating that a sign change means there's a solution]

    b) $3x - 2x^3 + 5 = 0$
         $2x^3 = 3x + 5$ *[1 mark]*
         $x^3 = \dfrac{3x + 5}{2}$ *[1 mark]*

         $x = \sqrt[3]{\dfrac{3x + 5}{2}}$ *[1 mark]*

         [3 marks available in total — as above]

    c) $x_0 = 2$ $x_1 = 1.765174...$
         $x_2 = 1.726657...$ $x_3 = 1.720173...$
         $x_4 = 1.719076...$ $x_5 = 1.718891...$
         $x_6 = 1.718860...$ $x_7 = 1.718854...$
         $x_8 = 1.718853...$
         $x_7 = x_8$ to 5 d.p. so $x = 1.71885$ to 5 d.p.
         [3 marks available — 1 mark for carrying out the iteration correctly, 1 mark for stopping when the x-values are equal to 5 d.p., 1 mark for the correct value of x]

Pages 34-35: Simultaneous Equations

1   $x + 3y = 11 \xrightarrow{\times 3} 3x + 9y = 33$ *[1 mark]*

    $\begin{aligned} 3x + 9y &= 33 \\ \underline{3x + y} &= \underline{9 -} \\ 8y &= 24 \\ y &= 3 \end{aligned}$ *[1 mark]* $\begin{aligned} x + 3y &= 11 \\ x + (3 \times 3) &= 11 \\ x &= 11 - 9 \\ x &= 2 \end{aligned}$ *[1 mark]*

    [3 marks available in total — as above]
    For all the simultaneous equation questions, you could have eliminated the other variable and/or substituted into the other equation — you'd get the marks either way.

2   $2x + 3y = 12 \xrightarrow{\times 5} 10x + 15y = 60$ *[1 mark]*
    $5x + 4y = 9 \xrightarrow{\times 2} 10x + 8y = 18$ *[1 mark]*

    $\begin{aligned} 10x + 15y &= 60 \\ \underline{10x + 8y} &= \underline{18 -} \\ 7y &= 42 \\ y &= 6 \end{aligned}$ *[1 mark]* $\begin{aligned} 2x + 3y &= 12 \\ 2x &= 12 - (3 \times 6) \\ 2x &= -6 \\ x &= -3 \end{aligned}$ *[1 mark]*

    [4 marks available in total — as above]

3   Let f be the number of chocolate frogs and m be
    the number of sugar mice.
    $4f + 3m = £3.69$ and $6f + 2m = £3.96$ *[1 mark]*
    $4f + 3m = £3.69 \xrightarrow{\times 2} 8f + 6m = £7.38$
    $6f + 2m = £3.96 \xrightarrow{\times 3} 18f + 6m = £11.88$

    $\begin{aligned} 18f + 6m &= £11.88 \\ \underline{8f + 6m} &= \underline{£7.38 -} \\ 10f &= £4.50 \\ f &= £0.45 \end{aligned}$ *[1 mark]* $\begin{aligned} 4f + 3m &= £3.69 \\ 3m &= £3.69 - (4 \times 0.45) \\ 3m &= £1.89 \\ m &= £0.63 \end{aligned}$ *[1 mark]*

    So a bag with 2 chocolate frogs and 5 sugar mice would cost
    $(2 \times 0.45) + (5 \times 0.63) = £4.05$ *[1 mark]*
    [4 marks available in total — as above]

4   $x^2 + y = 4$, so $y = 4 - x^2$
    $4x - 1 = 4 - x^2$ *[1 mark]*
    $x^2 + 4x - 5 = 0$ *[1 mark]*
    $(x + 5)(x - 1) = 0$ *[1 mark]*
    $x = -5$ or $x = 1$ *[1 mark]*
    When $x = 1$, $y = (4 \times 1) - 1 = 3$
    When $x = -5$, $y = (4 \times -5) - 1 = -21$
    So the solutions are $x = 1, y = 3$ and $x = -5, y = -21$ *[1 mark]*
    [5 marks available in total — as above]

5   $y = x + 6$, so $2x^2 + (x + 6)^2 = 51$ *[1 mark]*
    $2x^2 + x^2 + 12x + 36 = 51$
    $3x^2 + 12x - 15 = 0$ *[1 mark]*
    $(3x - 3)(x + 5) = 0$ *[1 mark]*
    $x = 1$ or $x = -5$ *[1 mark]*
    When $x = 1$, $y = 1 + 6 = 7$
    When $x = -5$, $y = -5 + 6 = 1$
    So the solutions are $x = 1, y = 7$ and $x = -5, y = 1$ *[1 mark]*
    [5 marks available in total — as above]

6   $y = x^2 + 3x - 1$ and $y = 2x + 5$ so $x^2 + 3x - 1 = 2x + 5$ *[1 mark]*
    $x^2 + x - 6 = 0$
    $(x + 3)(x - 2) = 0$ *[1 mark]*
    $x = -3$ or $x = 2$ *[1 mark]*
    When $x = -3$, $y = (2 \times -3) + 5 = -6 + 5 = -1$
    When $x = 2$, $y = (2 \times 2) + 5 = 9$
    So the lines intersect at $(-3, -1)$ and $(2, 9)$ *[1 mark]*
    Change in $x = 2 - (-3) = 5$
    Change in $y = 9 - (-1) = 10$ *[1 mark for both]*
    $\sqrt{10^2 + 5^2} = \sqrt{125} = 5\sqrt{5}$, so $k = 5$ *[1 mark]*
    [6 marks available in total — as above]

Page 36: Proof

1   $(3n + 2)^2 - (n + 2)^2 = (3n + 2)(3n + 2) - (n + 2)(n + 2)$
    $= (9n^2 + 12n + 4) - (n^2 + 4n + 4)$
    $= 9n^2 + 12n + 4 - n^2 - 4n - 4$ *[1 mark]*
    $= 8n^2 + 8n$
    $= 8n(n + 1)$ *[1 mark]*
    [2 marks available in total — as above]

2 E.g. When $a = 1$, $b = 2$, $c = 3$ and $d = 10$ then
$a < b < c < d$
$\frac{a}{b} = \frac{1}{2}$ and $\frac{c}{d} = \frac{3}{10}$ but $\frac{1}{2} > \frac{3}{10}$ so $\frac{a}{b} > \frac{c}{d}$
which contradicts what Jake says so Jake is not correct.
*[3 marks available — 1 mark for finding values of a, b, c and d,
1 mark for showing that these values form a counterexample,
1 mark for stating that Jake is wrong]*

3 n is an integer. $2n$ represents any even number, so the difference
between the squares of two consecutive even numbers will be given
by $(2n + 2)^2 - (2n)^2$.
$(2n + 2)^2 - (2n)^2 = (4n^2 + 8n + 4) - 4n^2$
$= 8n + 4 = 4(2n + 1)$
$= 4x$ (where x is an integer given by $x = 2n + 1$)
Any integer multiplied by 4 is a multiple of 4, so $4x$ must be a
multiple of 4 and therefore the difference between the squares of
two consecutive even numbers will always be a multiple of 4.
*[3 marks available — 1 mark for finding an expression for the
difference between the squares, 1 mark for rearranging into the
form 4(2x + 1), 1 mark for conclusion]*

4 If $2^{64} - 1$ is prime then it's only factors are 1 and itself
$2^{64} - 1 = (2^{32})^2 - 1^2 = (2^{32} + 1)(2^{32} - 1)$ *[1 mark]*
So $(2^{32} + 1)$ and $(2^{32} - 1)$ are factors of $2^{64} - 1$ *[1 mark]*
But neither $(2^{32} + 1)$ or $(2^{32} - 1)$ are equal to 1 or $2^{64} - 1$
so $2^{64} - 1$ cannot be prime. *[1 mark]*
[3 marks available in total — as above]

Page 37: Functions

1 a) $f(7.5) = \frac{3}{2(7.5) + 5} = \frac{3}{20} = 0.15$ *[1 mark]*

   b) Write out $x = f(y)$, $x = \frac{3}{2y + 5}$ *[1 mark]*
   Rearrange to make y the subject:
   $2y + 5 = \frac{3}{x}$
   $2y = \frac{3}{x} - 5$ *[1 mark]*
   $y = \frac{3}{2x} - \frac{5}{2}$ so $f^{-1}(x) = \frac{3}{2x} - \frac{5}{2}$ *[1 mark]*
   [3 marks available in total — as above]

   c) $ff^{-1}(x) = \frac{3}{2\left(\frac{3}{2x} - \frac{5}{2}\right) + 5}$ *[1 mark]*
   $= \frac{3}{\left(\frac{3}{x} - 5 + 5\right)} = \frac{3}{\left(\frac{3}{x}\right)}$ *[1 mark]*
   $= 3 \times \frac{x}{3} = x$ *[1 mark]*
   [3 marks available in total — as above]

2 a) $g(21) = \sqrt{2 \times 21 - 6} = \sqrt{36} = 6$ *[1 mark]*

   b) $gf(x) = g(f(x)) = \sqrt{2(2x^2 + 3) - 6}$ *[1 mark]*
   $= \sqrt{4x^2 + 6 - 6}$
   $= \sqrt{4x^2}$
   $= 2x$ *[1 mark]*
   [2 marks available in total — as above]

   c) $fg(a) = f(g(a)) = 2(\sqrt{2a - 6})^2 + 3$ *[1 mark]*
   $= 2(2a - 6) + 3$
   $= 4a - 9$ *[1 mark]*
   So when $fg(a) = 7$, $4a - 9 = 7$
   $a = 4$ *[1 mark]*
   [3 marks available in total — as above]

Section Three — Graphs

Pages 38-39: Straight Line Graphs

1 a) Using $y = mx + c$, where m is the gradient,
   and c is the y-intercept:
   $m = \frac{(7 - (-3))}{(5 - 0)}$
   $m = 2$ *[1 mark]*
   When $x = 0$, $y = -3$, so $c = -3$ *[1 mark]*
   So, $y = 2x - 3$ *[1 mark]*
   [3 marks available in total — as above]

   b) Using gradient from part a), $m = 2$
   When $x = 2$, $y = 10$, so
   $10 = (2 \times 2) + c$
   i.e. $c = 6$ *[1 mark]*
   So, $y = 2x + 6$ *[1 mark]*
   [2 marks available in total — as above]

   c) Difference in x-coordinate from A to B: $5 - 0 = 5$
   Difference in y-coordinate from A to B: $7 - (-3) = 10$
   So the x-coordinate of P: $0 + \frac{2}{5} \times 5 = 2$
   and the y-coordinate of P: $-3 + \frac{2}{5} \times 10 = 1$
   The coordinates of P are (2, 1).
   *[3 marks available — 1 mark for correct difference in x
   and y-coordinates, 1 mark for correctly multiplying by $\frac{2}{5}$,
   1 mark for correct coordinates]*

2 $3x + 4 = 2x + 6$ *[1 mark]*
   $x = 2$ *[1 mark]*
   so $y = 3(2) + 4 = 10$ and point M is (2, 10) *[1 mark]*
   Gradient of line **N** $= \frac{1}{2}$ (as it's parallel),
   so $y = \frac{1}{2}x + c$ *[1 mark]*
   $10 = \frac{1}{2} \times 2 + c$, so $c = 10 - 1 = 9$
   $y = \frac{1}{2}x + 9$ *[1 mark]*
   [5 marks available in total — as above]

3 a) $2a + 4 = 2c$, so $a + 2 = c$
   Substitute values $a + 2 = c$ and $b - 6 = d$ into point (c, d):
   $(c, d) = (a + 2, b - 6)$
   Gradient of **S** $= \frac{b - 6 - b}{a + 2 - a} = \frac{-6}{2} = -3$
   *[3 marks available — 1 mark for correctly substituting values
   into a point, 1 mark for finding change in y over change in x,
   1 mark for correct answer]*

   b) Gradient $= \frac{1}{3}$ *[1 mark]*
   So $y = \frac{1}{3}x + c$.
   Substitute (6, 3) into the equation:
   $3 = \frac{1}{3} \times 6 + c$
   $c = 1$
   Line **R**: $y = \frac{1}{3}x + 1$ *[1 mark]*
   [2 marks available in total — as above]

4 Midpoint of line AB: $\left(\frac{5 + 1}{2}, \frac{7 - 1}{2}\right) = (3, 3)$
   Midpoint of line CD: $\left(\frac{13 + 3}{2}, \frac{4 - 2}{2}\right) = (8, 1)$
   Gradient of line AB: $\frac{7 - (-1)}{5 - 1} = \frac{8}{4} = 2$
   Gradient of the line joining the midpoints of AB and CD:
   Gradient $= \frac{1 - 3}{8 - 3} = \frac{-2}{5}$
   $\frac{-1}{2} \neq \frac{-2}{5}$, therefore James is incorrect.
   *[4 marks available — 1 mark for saying James is wrong,
   1 mark for finding both midpoints, 1 mark for finding both
   gradients, 1 mark for comparing gradients to show that the
   lines aren't perpendicular]*

Pages 40-41: Quadratic Graphs

1 a) $(1.5, -0.25)$ *[1 mark]*

   If your y-coordinate is between −0.23 and −0.28 you'll get the marks.

   b) $a = 2$ *[1 mark]*

2 a)

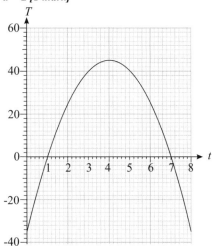

[3 marks available — 1 mark for plotting correct values, 1 mark for drawing a smooth curve through these points, 1 mark for correct intersections and turning point]

   b) $t = 4$ *[1 mark]*

   c) $t = 1.8, t = 6.2$

   [2 marks available — 1 mark for each solution (allow answers ±0.2)]

3 To find intersections with the x-axis, solve $2x^2 + 10x - 12 = 0$:
   $x^2 + 5x - 6 = 0$
   $(x + 6)(x - 1) = 0$ so $x = -6, x = 1$
   So the x-intercepts are $(-6, 0)$ and $(1, 0)$
   To find where the graph crosses the y-axis, substitute $x = 0$ into the equation: $y = 0 + 0 - 12 = -12$
   So the y-intercept is $(0, -12)$

   Use symmetry and the x-intercepts to find the turning point
   of the curve: $x = \dfrac{1 + (-6)}{2} = -2.5$
   $y = 2(-2.5)^2 + 10(-2.5) - 12 = -24.5$
   So the turning point lies at $(-2.5, -24.5)$

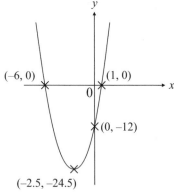

[4 marks available in total — 1 mark for correct shaped curve, 1 mark for correctly labelled turning point, 1 mark for correctly labelled y-intercept and 1 mark for correctly labelled x-intercepts]

You can also find the turning point by completing the square.

4 Complete the square: $(x - 2)^2 = x^2 - 4x + 4$ *[1 mark]*
   $(x - 2)^2 + 2 = x^2 - 4x + 6$
   So the completed square is $f(x) = (x - 2)^2 + 2$ *[1 mark]*
   So the turning point is $(2, 2)$ *[1 mark for each coordinate]*
   [4 marks available in total — as above]

Pages 42-43: Harder Graphs

1 a) B *[1 mark]*

   b) C *[1 mark]*

   c) A *[1 mark]*

2 a)

x	2.5	3	3.5	4
y	−5.375	−5	−2.125	4

[2 marks available — 2 marks for all answers correct, otherwise 1 mark for two correct answers]

   b)

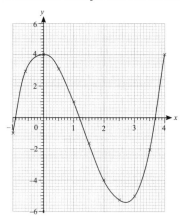

[2 marks available — 1 mark for plotting correct points, 1 mark for joining them with a smooth curve]

   c) Reading off the graph, where the curve intersects the x-axis, $x = -0.9$, $x = 1.2$ and $x = 3.7$ *[1 mark]*

   You'll get the mark if your answers are within 0.1 of the answer.

3 a)

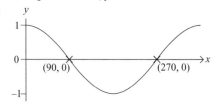

[2 marks available — 1 mark for curve fluctuating between 1 and −1 on the y-axis, 1 mark for correctly labelled intersections]

   b)

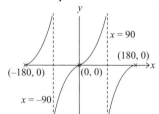

[3 marks available — 1 mark for correct shaped curve, 1 mark for correctly labelled intersections, 1 mark for showing tan x is undefined at x = −90 and x = 90]

4 a) No, the curve will not pass through the origin.
      It is a circle equation, centred at $(0, 0)$ with radius 4.
      [2 marks available — 1 mark for correct answer, 1 mark for suitable explanation or graph]

   b) $x = -4, x = 4$ *[1 mark]*

Pages 44: Solving Equations from Graphs

1 The graphs cross at $(0.5, -4)$ and $(4, 3)$, so the solutions are
   $x = 0.5, y = -4$ *[1 mark]*
   and $x = 4, y = 3$ *[1 mark]*

   [2 marks available in total — as above]

2 Find the equation of the line that should be drawn:
$x^2 + x = 6$
$x^2 + x - 5 = 1$
$x^2 + 2x - 5 = x + 1$
So draw the line $y = x + 1$ to find the solutions *[1 mark]*

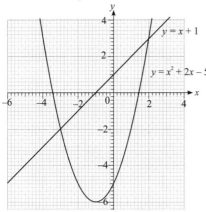

[1 mark]

The solutions to $x^2 + x = 6$ are:
$x = -3$ *[1 mark]*
$x = 2$ *[1 mark]*

[4 marks available in total — as above]

Pages 45-46: Graph Transformations

1 a)

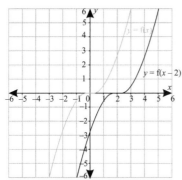

[2 marks available — 2 marks for the correct curve shifted 2 units to the right, otherwise 1 mark for an incorrect curve shifted 2 units to the right]

b) (2, 0) *[1 mark]*

2 a) $y = f(x + 1) - 2$ is the graph $y = f(x)$ shifted left by 1 unit and down by 2 units. The transformed graph crosses the x-axis twice, so yes, $y = f(x + 1) - 2$ has real roots.
The roots are found at $(-4, 0)$ and $(-1, 0)$.
[2 marks available — 1 mark for each root]

b) The minimum point of $f(x)$ is approximately $(-1.5, -0.25)$
To find the minimum point of $y = f(x - 4) + 1$ do
$(-1.5 + 4, -0.25 + 1)$
So the minimum point of $y = f(x - 4) + 1$ is $(2.5, 0.75)$
[3 marks available — 1 mark for finding a minimum point, 1 mark for each correct transformed coordinate].

3 a)

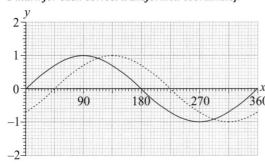

[1 mark]

b)

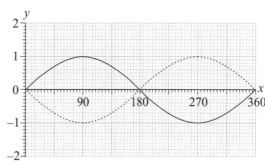

[1 mark]

4 a)

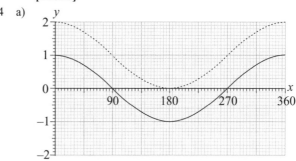

[2 marks available — 1 mark for correct graph shape, 1 mark for correct position]

b) $x = 90° - 30° = 60°$ and $x = 270° - 30° = 240°$
[2 marks available — 1 mark for each correct answer]
cos x crosses the x-axis at x = 90° and x = 270°.
The reflection doesn't change the x-intercepts, but the translation shifts the graph 30° left (or −30° right).

Page 47: Real-life Graphs

1 a) Plan A: £25 *[1 mark]*
Plan B: £28 *[1 mark]*
[2 marks available in total — as above]

b) Mr Barker should use Plan A because it is cheaper. Using 85 units with Plan A would cost £26.50. 85 units with Plan B would cost £34.
[2 marks available — 1 mark for correctly stating which plan, 1 mark for giving a reason]

2 Graph A and 2, Graph B and 3
Graph C and 4, Graph D and 1
[2 marks available — 2 marks for all four correct pairs, otherwise 1 mark for two correct pairs]

Page 48: Distance-Time Graphs

1 a) 1 hour *[1 mark]*

b) Tyrone. He reaches 30 km after 5 hours whereas Selby reaches 30 km after 6 hours. *[1 mark]*

c) Gradient = $\dfrac{\text{change in } y}{\text{change in } x} = \dfrac{25 - 15}{3 - 1.5} = \dfrac{10}{1.5} = 6.67$ km/h (2 d.p)
[2 marks available — 2 marks for correct answer, otherwise 1 mark for choosing correct x and y values]

d) E.g. Selby is the most likely to have been injured.
The gradient of Selby's line decreases towards the end of the race, whereas Tyrone's gets much steeper. This means Selby was moving much more slowly than Tyrone towards the end of the race. *[2 marks available — 1 mark for stating Selby is the injured runner, 1 mark for a correct explanation referring to gradients or steepness of lines]*

Page 49: Velocity-Time Graphs

1 a)

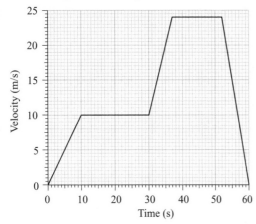

[3 marks available — 3 marks for fully correct graph, otherwise 2 marks for 2 non-horizontal sections correct, or 1 mark for 1 non-horizontal section correct]

b) At 35 seconds the graph has a gradient of $\frac{24-10}{37-30} = \frac{14}{7} = 2$. Acceleration = 2 m/s². *[1 mark]*

2 E.g.

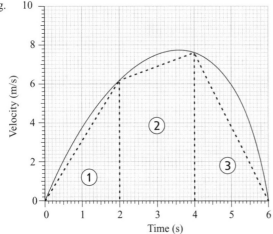

Area of triangle 1: $\frac{1}{2} \times 6.2 \times 2 = 6.2$ m

Area of trapezium 2: $\frac{1}{2} \times (6.2 + 7.6) \times 2 = 13.8$ m

Area of triangle 3: $\frac{1}{2} \times 7.6 \times 2 = 7.6$ m

Approximate distance travelled = 6.2 + 13.8 + 7.6 = 27.6 m

Estimate of average speed = 27.6 ÷ 6 = 5 m/s (1 s.f.)

[4 marks available — 1 mark for attempting to split up the area under the curve, 1 mark for correctly finding the area of 2 or more shapes, 1 mark for using total distance to find the average speed and 1 mark for the correct final answer]

If you've split the shape up differently you'll get a different answer. As long as you've done the correct working for your shapes you'll get the marks.

Page 50: Gradients of Curves

1 a)

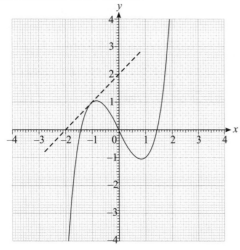

Gradient = $\frac{2-0}{0-(-2)} = \frac{2}{2} = 1$

[2 marks available — 2 marks for the correct answer, otherwise 1 mark for correctly drawing the tangent]

b)

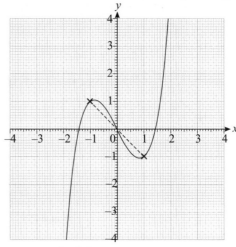

Gradient = $\frac{1-(-1)}{-1-1} = \frac{2}{-2} = -1$

[2 marks available — 2 marks for the correct answer, otherwise 1 mark for correctly drawing a line connecting (-1, 1) and (1, -1)]

2 a)

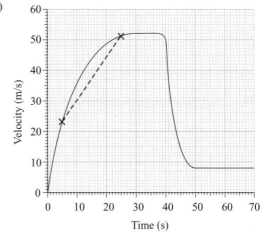

Gradient = $\frac{51-23}{25-5} = \frac{28}{20} = 1.4$ m/s²

[2 marks available — 2 marks for the correct answer, otherwise 1 mark for correctly drawing a line connecting (5, 23) and (25, 51)]

b)

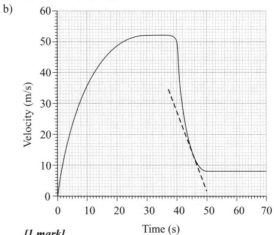

[1 mark]

Gradient = $\frac{27-2}{40-50} = \frac{25}{-10} = -2.5$ m/s² *[1 mark]*

[2 marks available — 2 marks for answer between −2 and −3, otherwise 1 mark for correctly drawing the tangent]

Answers

Section Four —
Ratio, Proportion and Rates of Change

Pages 51-53: Ratios

1   Longest – shortest = 7 – 5 = 2 parts = 9 cm *[1 mark]*
   1 part = 9 ÷ 2 = 4.5 cm
   Original piece of wood is 5 + 6 + 6 + 7 = 24 parts *[1 mark]*
   So, the original piece of wood is 24 × 4.5 = 108 cm *[1 mark]*
   [3 marks available in total — as above]

2   a) $3\frac{3}{4} : 1\frac{1}{2} = 4 \times 3\frac{3}{4} : 4 \times 1\frac{1}{2} = 15 : 6$ *[1 mark]*
                          $= 5 : 2$ *[1 mark]*
       [2 marks available in total — as above]

   b)   5 + 2 = 7 parts
       1 part: 2800 ml ÷ 7 = 400 ml
       Yellow paint = 400 ml × 5 = 2000 ml
       Blue paint = 400 ml × 2 = 800 ml
       [2 marks available — 1 mark for finding the amount of 1 part, 1 mark for finding the correct amounts for both yellow and blue paint]
       If your answer to part a) was incorrect, but your answers to part b) were correct for your incorrect ratio, you still get the marks for part b).

3   Edmund, Susan and Peter shared the money in the ratio
   $4x + 10 : 2x + 5 : 5x + 3$
   $(4x + 10) + (2x + 5) + (5x + 3) = 150$
   $11x + 18 = 150$
   $11x = 132$
   $x = 12$
   Edmund: (4 × 12) + 10 = £58
   Susan: (2 × 12) + 5 = £29
   Peter: (5 × 12) + 3 = £63
   [4 marks available — 1 mark for forming equation from ratios, 1 mark for finding the value of x, 1 mark for the correct amount for one person, 1 mark for finding the correct amount for the other two people]

4   a) $\frac{2}{9}$ as much milk is used as ice cream *[1 mark]*
   b)   1 part: 801 ÷ 9 = 89 ml *[1 mark]*
       9 + 2 = 11 parts
       89 × 11 = 979 ml *[1 mark]*
       [2 marks available in total — as above]
   c)   E.g.
       Find a point on the graph:
       When ice cream = 900 ml, milk = $900 \times \frac{2}{9} = 200$ ml

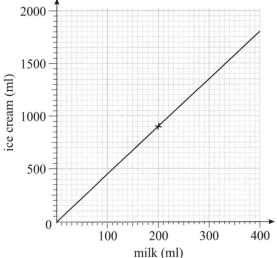

       [2 marks available — 1 mark for plotting any point on the line correctly, 1 mark for a straight line that passes through that point and (0, 0)]

5   16 kg of Mr Appleseed's Supercompost contains:
   $\frac{4}{8} \times 16 = 8$ kg of soil.
   $\frac{3}{8} \times 16 = 6$ kg of compost.
   $\frac{1}{8} \times 16 = 2$ kg of grit.
   Soil costs £8 ÷ 40 = £0.20 per kg.
   Compost costs £15 ÷ 25 = £0.60 per kg.
   Grit costs £12 ÷ 15 = £0.80 per kg.
   16 litres of Mr Appleseed's Supercompost costs:
   (8 × 0.2) + (6 × 0.6) + (2 × 0.8) = £6.80
   Profit: £10 – £6.80 = £3.20
   [5 marks available — 1 mark for the correct mass of one ingredient, 1 mark for the correct masses for the other two ingredients, 1 mark for working out the price per kg for each ingredient, 1 mark for the total cost of 16 kg of Supercompost, 1 mark for the correct answer]

6   $x - 5 : y - 3 = 5 : 8$ and $x + 5 : y + 7 = 5 : 7$ *[1 mark]*
   $\frac{x-5}{y-3} = \frac{5}{8}$ and $\frac{x+5}{y+7} = \frac{5}{7}$ *[1 mark]*
   $8(x - 5) = 5(y - 3)$ and $7(x + 5) = 5(y + 7)$
   Expand and simplify to give:
   $8x - 5y = 25$ [1] and $7x - 5y = 0$ [2] *[1 mark]*
   [1] – [2]: $x = 25$ *[1 mark]*
   Sub into [1]: $(8 \times 25) - 5y = 25$
                $5y = 175$, so $y = 35$ *[1 mark]*
   Solution: $x = 25$, $y = 35$
   [5 marks available in total — as above]

7   Call the number of black olives b and the number of green olives g.
   $b : g = 5 : 11$ and $b - 3 : g - 1 = 3 : 7$ *[1 mark for both]*
   $\frac{b}{g} = \frac{5}{11}$ and $\frac{b-3}{g-1} = \frac{3}{7}$ *[1 mark for both]*
   $11b = 5g$ and $7(b - 3) = 3(g - 1)$
   $11b - 5g = 0$ [1] and $7b - 3g = 18$ [2] *[1 mark]*
   [1] × 3: $33b - 15g = 0$ [3]
   [2] × 5: $35b - 15g = 90$ [4] *[1 mark for both]*
   [4] – [3]: $2b = 90$
             $b = 45$ *[1 mark]*
   Sub into [1]: $(11 \times 45) - 5g = 0$
                $5g = 495$, so $g = 99$ *[1 mark]*
   Solution: $b = 45$, $g = 99$
   [6 marks available in total — as above]
   You might have started with $\frac{b}{b+g} = \frac{5}{16}$ and $\frac{b-3}{b+g-4} = \frac{3}{10}$ and used these to form simultaneous equations instead.

Pages 54-55: Direct and Inverse Proportion

1   1 t-shirt will take: 5 m² ÷ 8 = 0.625 m² of cotton *[1 mark]*
   85 t-shirts will take: 0.625 m² × 85 = 53.125 m² of cotton *[1 mark]*
   1 m² of cotton costs: £5.50 ÷ 2 = £2.75 *[1 mark]*
   53.125 m² of cotton costs £2.75 × 53.125 = £146.09375
                                          = £146.09 *[1 mark]*
   [4 marks available in total — as above]

2   To harvest the same amount as Neil, Sophie will take:
   3.5 hours ÷ 2 = 1.75 hours *[1 mark]*
   Sophie needs to harvest three times as much so it will take her:
   1.75 × 3 *[1 mark]* = 5.25 hours *[1 mark]*
   [3 marks available in total — as above]

3   a)   1 litre of petrol will keep 8 go-karts going for:
       20 ÷ 12 = 1.666... minutes *[1 mark]*
       18 litres of petrol will keep 8 go-karts going for:
       1.666... × 18 = 30 minutes *[1 mark]*
       18 litres of petrol will keep 1 go-kart going for:
       30 × 8 = 240 minutes *[1 mark]*
       18 litres of petrol will keep 6 go-karts going for:
       240 ÷ 6 = 40 minutes *[1 mark]*
       [4 marks available in total — as above]
       You might have done these steps in a slightly different order — you'd still get all the marks as long as you got the same answer.

b) In 1 minute, 8 go-karts will use $12 \div 20 = 0.6$ litres *[1 mark]*
In 45 minutes, 8 go-karts will use
$0.6 \times 45 = 27$ litres *[1 mark]*
27 litres of petrol cost: $£1.37 \times 27 = £36.99$ *[1 mark]*
[3 marks available in total — as above]

4

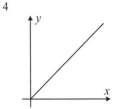 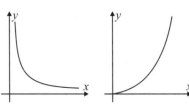

[3 marks available — 1 mark for each correct graph]

5 $f \propto \dfrac{1}{d^2}$, so $f = \dfrac{k}{d^2}$ *[1 mark]*
When $d = 100$ and $f = 20$, $20 = \dfrac{k}{100^2}$,
so $k = 20 \times 100^2 = 200\,000$ *[1 mark]*
$f = \dfrac{200\,000}{d^2}$
When $d = 800$, $f = \dfrac{200\,000}{800^2} = 0.3125$ *[1 mark]*
[3 marks available in total — as above]

6 a) $h \propto S^2$, so $h = kS^2$ *[1 mark]*
When $h = 35$ and $S = 50$, $35 = k \times 50^2$,
so $k = 35 \div 50^2 = 0.014$ *[1 mark]*
So $h = 0.014S^2$
$h = 0.014S^2$ so when $S = 40$, $h = 0.014 \times 40^2 = 22.4$ *[1 mark]*
[3 marks available in total — as above]

b) If h_0 is the initial height difference, S_0 is the initial speed and h_1 is the changed height difference, then:
$h_0 = k(S_0)^2$
$h_1 = k(1.3S_0)^2$ *[1 mark]*
$= 1.69k(S_0)^2$ *[1 mark]* $= 1.69h_0$ *[1 mark]*
So the height needs to be increased by 69%. *[1 mark]*
[4 marks available in total — as above]

Pages 56-58: Percentages

1 $20\% = 20 \div 100 = 0.2$
$0.2 \times £927 = £185.40$ *[1 mark]*
$£927 + £185.40$ *[1 mark]*
$= £1112.40$ *[1 mark]*
[3 marks available in total — as above]

2 For every 2 grapes there are 5 cherries so there are $\dfrac{2}{5} = 40\%$ as many grapes as cherries. *[1 mark]*

3 $£15\,714 = 108\%$
$£15\,714 \div 108 = £145.50 = 1\%$ *[1 mark]*
$£145.50 \times 100 = 100\%$ *[1 mark]*
$= £14\,550$ *[1 mark]*
[3 marks available in total — as above]

4 $£41\,865 - £10\,000 = £31\,865$
$20\% = 20 \div 100 = 0.2$
20% of $£31\,865 = 0.2 \times £31\,865 = £6373$ *[1 mark]*
$£45\,000 - £41\,865 = £3135$
$40\% = 40 \div 100 = 0.4$
40% of $£3135 = 0.4 \times £3135 = £1254$ *[1 mark]*
$£6373 + £1254 = £7627$
$(£7627 \div £45\,000) \times 100$ *[1 mark]*
$= 16.948... = 16.9\%$ (1 d.p) *[1 mark]*
[4 marks available in total — as above]

5 a) 40% of $50\% = 0.4 \times 50\%$ *[1 mark]*
$= 20\%$ *[1 mark]*
[2 marks available in total — as above]

b) 20% of the animals are black cats so:
$100\% - 20\% = 80\%$ are not black cats *[1 mark]*
80% of $90 = 90 \times 0.8 = 72$ *[1 mark]*
[2 marks available in total — as above]

6 $£32$ is a 60% profit so $£32 = 160\%$ of cost price *[1 mark]*
1% of cost price $= £32 \div 160 = £0.20$ *[1 mark]*
He wants an 88% profit $= 188\%$ of cost price
$188\% = £0.20 \times 188 = £37.60$ *[1 mark]*
[3 marks available in total — as above]

7 a) Original price $= £180$, change in price $= £5.40$
Percentage increase $= \dfrac{£5.40}{£180} \times 100 = 3\%$
[2 marks available — 1 mark for using the correct formula, 1 mark for the correct answer]

b) Buying tickets in 1 transaction:
$(3 \times £180) + £5.40 = £545.40$
Buying tickets in 3 transactions:
$(£180 + £5.40) \times 3 = £556.20$
Decrease in cost $= £556.20 - £545.40 = £10.80$ *[1 mark]*
Percentage decrease $= \dfrac{£10.80}{£556.20} \times 100$ *[1 mark]*
$= 1.9417...\% = 1.94\%$ (2 d.p.) *[1 mark]*
[3 marks available in total — as above]
Careful here — the percentage saving is actually a percentage change, where the change is the saving and the original amount is the cost of the three separate transactions.

8 A ratio of $3:7$ means that 3 out of $10 = 30\%$ of the customers were children.
60% of $30\% = 0.6 \times 30\% = 18\%$ were blond-haired children.
$100\% - 30\% = 70\%$ were adults.
20% of $70\% = 0.2 \times 70\% = 14\%$ were blond-haired adults.
So, $18\% + 14\% = 32\%$ of the customers had blond hair.
[4 marks available — 1 mark for finding blond-haired children %, 1 mark for finding blond-haired adults %, 1 mark for adding together the two percentages, 1 mark for correct answer]

9 a) Original area of triangular face $= \dfrac{1}{2} \times x \times x = 0.5x^2$ cm^2
Area after increase $= \dfrac{1}{2} \times 1.15x \times 1.15x$
$= 0.66125x^2$ cm^2 *[1 mark]*
Change in area $= 0.66125x^2 - 0.5x^2 = 0.16125x^2$ cm^2 *[1 mark]*
Percentage increase $= \dfrac{0.16125x^2}{0.5x^2} \times 100$ *[1 mark]*
$= 32.25\%$ *[1 mark]*
[4 marks available in total — as above]
You could have found the new area by doing $0.5 \times 1.15x \times 1.15x$ $= 1.15^2 \times 0.5x^2 = 1.3225 \times$ original area, which means the percentage change is 32.25%.

b) Let ay cm be the length of the new prism.
Volume of new prism $= 0.66125x^2 \times ay$ *[1 mark]*
Volume of original prism $= 0.5x^2y$ cm^3
The prisms have the same volume so:
$0.66125x^2 \times ay = 0.5x^2y$ *[1 mark]*
$a = \dfrac{0.5x^2y}{0.66125x^2y}$
$a = 0.7561...$ *[1 mark]*
So the length of the new prism is $(0.7561... \times y)$ cm
$(1 - 0.7561) \times 100$ *[1 mark]*
$= 24.3856...\%$
$= 24.4\%$ decrease (1 d.p.) *[1 mark]*
[5 marks available in total — as above]

Pages 59-60: Compound Growth and Decay

1 Multiplier $= 1 + 0.06 = 1.06$ *[1 mark]*
In 3 years she will owe:
$£750 \times (1.06)^3 = £893.262$
$= £893.26$ (to the nearest penny) *[1 mark]*
[2 marks available in total — as above]

2 a) Multiplier $= 1 - 0.08 = 0.92$ *[1 mark]*
Population after 15 years $= 2000 \times (0.92)^{15}$
$= 572.59...$
≈ 573 fish *[1 mark]*
[2 marks available in total — as above]
It'll take more than 15 years for the population to get down to 572 fish, so you need to round up (the population hasn't dropped to 572 yet so there are still 573).

b) Three quarters of initial population = $2000 \times \frac{3}{4} = 1500$

$2000 \times 0.92 = 1840$

$2000 \times 0.92^2 = 1692.8$

$2000 \times 0.92^3 = 1557.376$

$2000 \times 0.92^4 = 1432.78592 < 1500$

Population is less than $\frac{3}{4}$ of the initial population after 4 years.

[2 marks available — 1 mark for calculating 2000×0.92^n for $n > 1$, 1 mark for correct answer]

3 $5000 \times 0.16 = 800$ trees are planted in 2013 *[1 mark]*

A maximum of $800 \times 0.75 = 600$ trees are cut down

At the end of 2013 there is a minimum of

$5000 + (800 - 600) = 5200$ pine trees *[1 mark]*

$5200 \times 0.16 = 832$ trees are planted in 2014 *[1 mark]*

A maximum of $832 \times 0.75 = 624$ trees are cut down

At the end of 2014 there is a minimum of

$5200 + (832 - 624) = 5408$ pine trees *[1 mark]*

[4 marks available in total — as above]

4 a) Compound Collectors Account:

Multiplier = $1 + 0.055 = 1.055$ *[1 mark]*

£10 000 $\times (1.055)^5 = $£13 069.60 (2 d.p.) *[1 mark]*

Simple Savers Account:

6.2% of £10 000 = $0.062 \times$ £10 000 = £620 *[1 mark]*

$5 \times$ £620 = £3100

£10 000 + £3100 = £13 100 so the Simple Savers Account will have the biggest balance after 5 years. *[1 mark]*

[4 marks available in total — as above]

b) E.g. He might want to deposit more money during the 5 years and he can't with the Simple Savers Account. *[1 mark]*

5 £2704 = £2500 $\times$ (Multiplier)^2 *[1 mark]*

$\frac{£2704}{£2500} = $ (Multiplier)^2

Multiplier $= \sqrt{\frac{£2704}{£2500}} = 1.04$ *[1 mark]*

Interest rate = $1.04 - 1 = 0.04 = 4\%$ *[1 mark]*

[3 marks available in total — as above]

6 Multiplier = $1 - 0.25 = 0.75$ *[1 mark]*

$N_0 \times (0.75)^{35-31} = 2\,000\,000$ *[1 mark]*

$N_0 = 2\,000\,000 \div 0.75^4 = 6\,320\,987.654...$

$= $£6 300 000 (to the nearest £100 000) *[1 mark]*

[3 marks available in total — as above]

Page 61: Speed

1 1 hour 15 minutes = 1.25 hours *[1 mark]*

Distance = speed $\times$ time, so distance = $56 \times 1.25 = 70$ km *[1 mark]*

[2 marks available in total — as above]

2 a) E.g. 2500 m = 2.5 km. 2.5 km = $2.5 \div 1.6 = 1.5625$ miles.

102 s $\div 60 = 1.7$ minutes $\div 60 = 0.02833...$ hours.

Speed = 1.5625 miles $\div 0.02833...$ hours

= 55 mph (to nearest mph)

[3 marks available — 1 mark for converting 2500 metres to miles, 1 mark for converting 102 seconds into hours, 1 mark for the correct final answer]

It doesn't matter whether you do the conversion to miles per hour at the start or the end of the calculation — you could find the speed in m/s, km/s or km/h, and then change it to mph. Whichever way, you should get the same answer.

b) E.g. time = 1.5625 miles $\div 50$ mph = 0.03125 hours

0.03125 hours $\times 60 \times 60 = 113$ s (to nearest second)

[2 marks available — 1 mark for dividing the distance by the speed limit, 1 mark for the correct answer]

3 In 2014 he finished with a time of $t - 0.1t = 0.9t$ *[1 mark]*

$s_1 = \frac{d}{t}$ and $s_2 = \frac{d}{0.9t}$ *[1 mark]*

So, $s_1 t = 0.9 s_2 t$

$s_2 = \frac{s_1}{0.9} = 1.111... \times s_1$ *[1 mark]*

So his percentage increase was 11.11% (2 d.p.) *[1 mark]*

[4 marks available in total — as above]

There are other methods to get to the correct answer — as long as you show full working and get the answer right then you'll get full marks.

Page 62: Density

1 a) Volume = $360 \div 1800$ *[1 mark]*

$= 0.2$ m^3 *[1 mark]*

[2 marks available in total — as above]

b) Density = $220 \div 0.2$ *[1 mark]*

$= 1100$ kg/m^3 *[1 mark]*

[2 marks available in total — as above]

2 a) Volume = 4 cm $\times$ 4 cm $\times$ 4 cm = 64 cm^3 *[1 mark]*

Mass = 7.9×64 *[1 mark]*

$= 505.6$ g *[1 mark]*

[3 marks available in total — as above]

b) 63.2 kg = 63 200 g *[1 mark]*

Volume of large cube: $63\,200 \div 7.9 = 8000$ cm^3 *[1 mark]*

Side length of large cube: $\sqrt[3]{8000} = 20$ cm *[1 mark]*

Ratio of side lengths of the smaller and larger cubes:

4 cm : 20 cm = 1 : 5 *[1 mark]*

[4 marks available in total — as above]

3 10 cm^3 of brass contains 7 cm^3 of copper and 3 cm^3 of zinc.

7 cm^3 of copper has a mass of $7 \times 8.9 = 62.3$ g

3 cm^3 of zinc has a mass of $3 \times 7.1 = 21.3$ g

10 cm^3 of brass has a mass of $62.3 + 21.3 = 83.6$ g

Density of brass = $83.6 \div 10 = 8.36$ g/cm^3

[4 marks available — 1 mark for finding the mass of a stated volume of copper or zinc, 1 mark for finding the total mass of a stated volume of brass, 1 mark for attempting to find density using total mass ÷ total volume and 1 mark for correct final answer]

Page 63: Pressure

1 a) Area of A = 40 cm $\times$ 20 cm = 800 cm^2

$= 800 \div 100 \div 100$

$= 0.08$ m^2 *[1 mark]*

Pressure = 40 N $\div 0.08$ m^2 *[1 mark]*

$= 500$ N/m^2 *[1 mark]*

[3 marks available in total — as above]

b) Three cuboids would have a weight of

3×40N = 120 N *[1 mark]*

Area of B = 3 m $\times$ 0.4 m = 1.2 m^2 *[1 mark]*

Pressure = 120 N $\div 1.2$ m^2 = 100 N/m^2 *[1 mark]*

[3 marks available in total — as above]

2 a) Area of circular base = $\pi \times (10x)^2 = 100\pi x^2$ cm^2 *[1 mark]*

$100\pi x^2$ cm^2 = $(100\pi x^2 \div 100 \div 100)$ m^2 = $0.01\pi x^2$ m^2 *[1 mark]*

Weight = $650 \times 0.01\pi x^2$ *[1 mark]* = $6.5\pi x^2$ N *[1 mark]*

[4 marks available in total — as above]

b) E.g. If the diameter is halved, the area of the circular base becomes: $\pi \times (5x)^2 = 25\pi x^2$ cm^2 = $0.0025\pi x^2$ m^2

Pressure = $6.5\pi x^2 \div 0.0025\pi x^2 = 2600$ N/m^2

2600 N/m$^2 \div 650$ N/m$^2 = 4$

If the diameter of the circle is halved the pressure increases and is 4 times greater.

[2 marks available — 1 mark for saying that the pressure increases, 1 mark for saying it's 4 times greater]

Section Five — Geometry and Measures

Pages 64-65: Geometry

1 Let a be the third angle in the triangle.

$a = 180° - y - z$ (angles in a triangle add to 180°) *[1 mark]*

$x = 180° - a$ (angles on a straight line add to 180°) *[1 mark]*

So $x = 180° - (180° - y - z) = y + z$ *[1 mark]*

[3 marks available in total — as above]

2 a) Angles on a straight line add up to 180°,

so angle $FEC = 180° - 14° = 166°$ *[1 mark]*

Angles in a quadrilateral add up to 360°,

so $x = 360° - 90° - 62° - 166° = 42°$ *[1 mark]*

[2 marks available in total — as above]

b) Angles in a triangle add up to 180° *[1 mark]*

so $y = 180° - 90° - 42° = 48°$ *[1 mark]*

[2 marks available in total — as above]

3   Let z be the top-left angle in the parallelogram.
x and z are allied angles, so $z = 180° - x$ *[1 mark]*
and y and z are allied angles, so $y = 180° - z$ *[1 mark]*.
So $y = 180° - (180° - x) = x$ *[1 mark]*
[3 marks available in total — as above]

4   Angles on a straight line add up to 180°,
so angle $ABJ = 180° - 140° = 40°$ *[1 mark]*
Allied angles add up to 180°,
so angle $JAB = 180° - 150° = 30°$ *[1 mark]*
Angles in a triangle add up to 180°,
so angle $AJB = 180° - 40° - 30° = 110°$ *[1 mark]*
Angles on a straight line add up to 180°,
so angle $x = 180° - 110° = 70°$ *[1 mark]*
[4 marks available in total — as above]

5   Angle BDC = angle $BCD = x$ (triangle BCD is isosceles)
Angle $CBD = 180° - x - x = 180° - 2x$ *[1 mark]*
(angles in a triangle add to 180°)
Angle BDE = angle $CBD = 180° - 2x$ *[1 mark]* (alternate angles)
Angle AED = angle $BDE = 180° - 2x$ *[1 mark]* ($ABDE$ is an
isosceles trapezium so has a vertical line of symmetry)
$y = 360°$ − angle AED *[1 mark]* (angles round a point add to 360°)
So $y = 360° - (180° - 2x) = 180° + 2x$ *[1 mark]*
[5 marks available in total — as above]

*There's more than one way to do the questions above — as long as
you show your working and explain each step you'll get the marks.*

6   $5x + (4x - 9°) = 180°$ *[1 mark]*
Rearranging this: $9x = 189°$
Therefore $x = 21°$ *[1 mark]*
$(4y - 12°) + 2y = 180°$ *[1 mark]*
Rearranging this: $6y = 192°$
Therefore $y = 32°$ *[1 mark]*
[4 marks available in total — as above]

Pages 66-67: Polygons

1   Rhombuses have two pairs of equal angles, so one of the other
angles must be 62°. *[1 mark]*
The sum of the angles in a quadrilateral is 360°, so the other angles
both equal $(360° - 62° - 62°) ÷ 2 = 118°$. *[1 mark]*
[2 marks available in total — as above]

2   Triangle ADX is isosceles, so angle DAX = angle $DXA = 41°$
and angle ADC = angle $ADX = 180° - 41° - 41° = 98°$ (angles in a
triangle sum to 180°). *[1 mark]*
Shape $ABCD$ is a kite, so angle ABC = angle $ADC = 98°$ *[1 mark]*
Sum of angles in a quadrilateral is 360° so
angle $DAB = 360° - 98° - 53° - 98° = 111°$ *[1 mark]*
[3 marks available in total — as above]

3   Exterior angle $= 180° - 150° = 30°$ *[1 mark]*
Number of sides $= 360° ÷ 30°$ *[1 mark]*
                 $= 12$ *[1 mark]*
[3 marks available in total — as above]

4   a) x is the same as an exterior angle, so $x = 360° ÷ 8$ *[1 mark]*
      $x = 45°$ *[1 mark]*
    [2 marks available in total — as above]

    b) $y = (180° - 45°) ÷ 2$ *[1 mark]*
      $y = 67.5°$ *[1 mark]*
    [2 marks available in total — as above]

5   Join the vertices of the hexagon to split it into triangles:

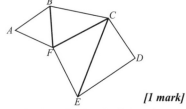

                        [1 mark]
The angles in each triangle add up to 180°,
so the sum of the interior angles of the hexagon is:
$4 × 180°$ *[1 mark]* $= 720°$ *[1 mark]*
[3 marks available in total — as above]

6   Interior angle of regular n-sided polygon $= 180°$ − exterior angle
                                   $= 180° - (360° ÷ n)$
Interior angle of regular octagon $= 180° - (360° ÷ 8) = 135°$
Interior angle of regular hexagon $= 180° - (360° ÷ 6) = 120°$
Angle CBK = angle ABC − angle $IJK = 135° - 120° = 15°$
*[2 marks available in total — 1 mark for using correct method
to find interior angle of octagon or hexagon, 1 mark for correct
answer]*

Pages 68-70: Circle Geometry

1   Angle $DBC = 62°$ *[1 mark]* (angles in the same segment are equal)
Angle $ABC = 90°$ *[1 mark]* (the angle in a semi-circle is 90°)
Angle $x = 90° - 62° = 28°$ *[1 mark]*
[3 marks available in total — as above]

2   Angle $DCO = 90°$ *[1 mark]* (tangent meets a radius at 90°)
Angle $DOC = 180° - 90° - 24° = 66°$ *[1 mark]* (angles in a triangle)
Angle $AOC = 66° × 2 = 132°$ *[1 mark]* (tangents from the same
point are the same length, so create two identical triangles)
Angle $ABC = 66°$ *[1 mark]* (angle at the centre is twice the angle
at the circumference)
Angle $CBE = 180° - 66° = 114°$ *[1 mark]* (angles on a straight line)
[5 marks available in total — as above]

3   Angle FBD = angle $BCD = 102°$
(alternate segment theorem) *[1 mark]*
Angle $CDB = 180° - 147° = 33°$
(angles on a straight line) *[1 mark]*
Angle $CBD = 180° - 102° - 33° = 45°$
(angles in a triangle) *[1 mark]*
Angle CAD = angle $CBD = 45°$
(angles in the same segment are equal) *[1 mark]*
[4 marks available in total — as above]

4   Angles ODE and OBE are both 90° because a tangent always meets
a radius at 90°. *[1 mark]*
Angle $DOB = 100°$ because angles in a quadrilateral add up to
360°. *[1 mark]*
Angle $DCB = 50°$ because an angle at the centre is twice the angle
at the circumference. *[1 mark]*
Angle $DAB = 130°$ because opposite angles of a cyclic
quadrilateral sum to 180°. *[1 mark]*
[4 marks available in total — as above]

5   Angle $DEG = 53°$ and angle $AEF = 37°$
(alternate segment theorem) *[1 mark]*
Angle $AED = 180° - 53° - 37° = 90°$
(angles on a straight line) *[1 mark]*
The chord AD must be a diameter of the circle (angle in a semi-circle
is 90°), so AD must pass through the centre of the circle. *[1 mark]*
[3 marks available in total — as above]

6   a)   Angle DAB = Angle $BDE = 53°$
      (alternate segment theorem) *[1 mark]*
      Angle $DOB = 2 ×$ Angle $DAB = 106°$ (angle at the centre
      is twice the angle at the circumference) *[1 mark]*
      [2 marks available in total — as above]
      *You could have done this one by splitting the triangle DOB into
      two identical right-angles triangles and working out the angles.*

    b) OB and OD are both radii, so OBD is an isosceles triangle.
      The radius OC crosses chord BD at right-angles, so it bisects
      BD *[1 mark]* and divides the isosceles triangle OBD in half,
      which means angle $COB = 0.5 ×$ angle DOB *[1 mark]*.
      [2 marks available in total — as above]

7   Opposite angles in a cyclic quadrilateral add up to 180°, so
angle $ADC = 180°$ − angle $ABC = 180° - 119° = 61°$
Angle CDX = angle ADC − angle $ADX = 61° - 31° = 30°$
If X was the centre of the circle, XD and XC would be radii, so
triangle CXD would be isosceles and angles CDX and XCD would
be equal. Here angle $CDX = 30°$ and angle $XCD = 28°$ so the
angles are not equal, and therefore X is not the centre of the circle.
*[3 marks available in total — 1 mark for finding angle ADC,
1 mark for finding angle CDX, 1 mark for using "two radii from
an isosceles triangle" to explain why X cannot be the centre.]*

Answers

Page 71: Congruent Shapes

1   F is the midpoint of AC so $AF = FC$ and opposite sides of a parallelogram are equal so $DE = FC$.
    Therefore $AF = DE$. *[1 mark]*
    E is the midpoint of CB so $CE = EB$, and opposite sides of a parallelogram are equal so $CE = FD$. Therefore $FD = EB$. *[1 mark]*
    D is the midpoint of AB, so $AD = DB$. *[1 mark]*
    Satisfies condition SSS so triangles are congruent. *[1 mark]*
    [4 marks available in total — as above]

2   E.g. $KP = OL$ (they are diameters of identical circles) *[1 mark]*
    Angle KMP = angle ONL
    (angles in a semicircle = 90°) *[1 mark]*
    Angle MKO = angle NLP
    (alternate angles in parallel lines are equal) *[1 mark]*
    Satisfies condition AAS so triangles are congruent. *[1 mark]*
    [4 marks available in total — as above]
    There are other ways you could have done this one — for example, you could show that the condition RHS holds.

3   Angle CAE = angle EBD
    (angles in the same segment are equal) *[1 mark]*
    Angle ACE = angle EDB
    (angles in the same segment are equal) *[1 mark]*
    $AC = DB$
    Satisfies condition AAS so triangles are congruent. *[1 mark]*
    [3 marks available in total — as above]

Page 72: Similar Shapes

1   a) Scale factor from $EFGH$ to $ABCD$ = 9 ÷ 6 = 1.5 *[1 mark]*
        EF = 6 ÷ 1.5 = 4 cm *[1 mark]*
        [2 marks available in total — as above]
    b) BC = 4 × 1.5 = 6 cm *[1 mark]*

2   63 m = 6300 cm
    Scale factor = 6300 ÷ 60 *[1 mark]*
             = 105 *[1 mark]*
    Height of flagpole = 8 cm × 105 = 840 cm = 8.4 m *[1 mark]*
    [3 marks available in total — as above]
    The triangles created between James' eyes and his finger and his eyes and the flagpole are similar.

3   Lines AD and EF are parallel (they're both parallel to BCG)
    Angles in a rectangle are 90° so angle ABC = angle CEF
    Corresponding angles are equal so angle BAC = angle ECF
    Corresponding angles are equal so angle ACB = angle CFE
    Triangles ABC and CEF have all three angles the same so are similar.
    [3 marks available — 1 mark for showing one angle is the same, 1 mark for showing that the rest are the same (the third angle can be implied from two angles the same), 1 mark for stating that the triangles are similar because their angles are the same]

Pages 73-74: The Four Transformations

1   a) $\begin{pmatrix} 2 \\ -5 \end{pmatrix}$

        [2 marks available — 1 mark for $\begin{pmatrix} \pm 2 \\ \pm 5 \end{pmatrix}$, 1 mark for fully correct answer]

    b)
    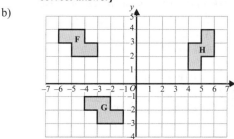

        [2 marks available — 1 mark for a rotation of 90° clockwise around any point, 1 mark for correct centre of rotation]

2   a) Rotation 90° anti-clockwise around the point (0, 0)
        [3 marks available — 1 mark for rotation, 1 mark for correct angle and direction of rotation, 1 mark for correct centre of rotation]

    b)
    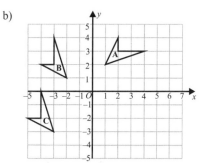

        [1 mark for correct translation]

3
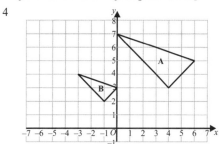

    [3 marks available — 3 marks for correct shape S in correct position, otherwise 1 mark for correctly reflected shape, 1 mark for one coordinate of shape S correct]

4
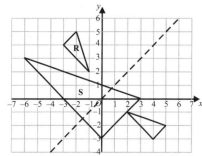

    [2 marks available — 2 marks for correct shape in correct position, otherwise 1 mark for one coordinate correct]

5
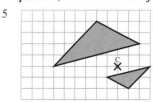

    [2 marks available — 2 marks for correct shape in correct position, otherwise 1 mark for one coordinate correct]

Pages 75-76: Perimeter and Area

1   Lawn area = (30 m × 10 m) − (π × (5 m)²) = 221.460... m²
    Boxes of seed needed = 221.460... m² ÷ 10 m² = 22.15
    So Lynn must buy 23 boxes. Total cost = 23 × £7 = £161
    [3 marks available — 1 mark for correctly calculating the lawn area, 1 mark for dividing the area by 10 m² to find the number of boxes, 1 mark for the correct answer]

2   Shorter parallel side of the trapezium
         = 52 cm − 16 cm − 16 cm = 20 cm
    To see this, split the shape into two triangles and a rectangle. The two triangles are both isosceles, so the base of each triangle is 16 cm long.
    Area of trapezium = 0.5 × (52 + 20) × 16 = 576 cm²
    [2 marks available — 1 mark for finding shorter parallel side of trapezium, 1 mark for correct answer]

3   Area of triangle = 0.5 × 2x × 2x = 2x^2 *[1 mark]*
    Area of square = x^2
    2x^2 − x^2 = 9 cm² *[1 mark]*
    x^2 = 9 cm² so x = 3 cm *[1 mark]*
    Perimeter of square = 4 × 3 cm = 12 cm *[1 mark]*
    [4 marks available in total — as above]

4 Let A have width x and length y.

Then B has width x and length $2y$.

The perimeter of C is $y + x + y + x + 2y + 2x = 4x + 4y$

and the perimeter of D is $x + 2y + x + 2y + (y - x) + x + y = 2x + 6y$

So, $4x + 4y = 28$ (1)

$2x + 6y = 34$ (2) $\xrightarrow{\times 2}$ $4x + 12y = 68$ (3)

(3) − (1): $8y = 40$, so $y = 5$ cm

Substitute into (1): $4x + 20 = 28$, so $x = 2$ cm

Perimeter of $A = 2 + 5 + 2 + 5 = 14$ cm

Perimeter of $B = 2 + 10 + 2 + 10 = 24$ cm

[6 marks available — 1 mark for setting up simultaneous equations, 1 mark for a correct method for finding one variable, 1 mark for a correct method for finding the other variable, 1 mark for using these values to find perimeters of A and B, 1 mark for perimeter of shape A correct, 1 mark for perimeter of shape B correct]

5 Circumference of full circle $= 2 \times \pi \times 6 = 12\pi$ cm

Length of arc $= (30 \div 360) \times$ circumference of circle

$= (30 \div 360) \times 12\pi = \pi$ cm

Perimeter of sector $= \pi + 6 + 6 = 15.1$ cm (3 s.f.)

Area of full circle $= \pi \times 6^2 = 36\pi$ cm²

Area of sector $= (30 \div 360) \times$ area of circle

$= (30 \div 360) \times 36\pi = 3\pi$ cm² $= 9.42$ cm² (3 s.f.)

[5 marks available — 1 mark for a correct method for calculating the length of the arc, 1 mark for correct arc length, 1 mark for correct perimeter of sector, 1 mark for a correct method for finding the area of the sector, 1 mark for correct area of sector]

6 Each straight section $= 2 \times$ radius $= 2 \times 9 = 18$ cm *[1 mark]*

Each curved section $= \frac{1}{3} \times$ circumference of circle

$= \frac{1}{3} \times 2 \times \pi \times 9$ *[1 mark]*

$= 6\pi$ cm *[1 mark]*

Total length $= 3 \times 18 + 3 \times 6\pi = 110.5$ cm (1 d.p.) *[1 mark]*

[4 marks available in total — as above]

Pages 77-79: 3D Shapes — Surface Area and Volume

1 Surface area of curved part of hemisphere =

½ × surface area of a sphere $= \frac{1}{2} \times 4 \times \pi \times 7^2$ *[1 mark]*

$= 307.876...$ cm²

Surface area of curved part of cone $= \pi \times 2 \times 12$ *[1 mark]*

$= 75.398...$ cm²

Surface area of flat top of hemisphere $= (\pi \times 7^2) - (\pi \times 2^2)$ *[1 mark]*

$= 141.371...$ cm²

Total surface area $= 307.876... + 75.398... + 141.371...$

$= 525$ cm² (to 3 s.f.) *[1 mark]*

[4 marks available in total — as above]

2 Slanting length of cone = 16 cm

Length of arc $= (90 \div 360) \times (2 \times \pi \times 16) = 8\pi$ *[1 mark]*

The circumference of the base $= 8\pi$, so the diameter of the base is $8\pi \div \pi = 8$. The radius is therefore $8 \div 2 = 4$ cm *[1 mark]*

Curved surface area of cone $= (\pi \times 4 \times 16)$ *[1 mark]*

Area of base of cone $= (\pi \times 4^2)$ *[1 mark]*

Total surface area of cone $= (\pi \times 4 \times 16) + (\pi \times 4^2)$

$= 80 \pi$ cm² *[1 mark]*

[5 marks available in total — as above]

3 Volume $= \frac{4}{3}\pi r^3 = 478$ cm³ *[1 mark]*

$r = \sqrt[3]{\frac{3 \times 478}{4\pi}} = 4.8504...$ cm *[1 mark]*

Surface area $= 4\pi r^2 = 4\pi \times (4.8504...)^2$ *[1 mark]*

$= 295.6$ cm² (1 d.p.) *[1 mark]*

[4 marks available in total — as above]

4 Volume $= \frac{1}{2} \times (\frac{4}{3} \times \pi \times 9^3) - \frac{1}{2} \times (\frac{4}{3} \times \pi \times 8^3)$ *[1 mark]*

$= 1526.814... - 1072.330...$ *[1 mark]* $= 454$ cm³ (3 s.f.) *[1 mark]*

[3 marks available in total — as above]

You still get full marks if you simplified the volume before multiplying everything through — e.g. you got $\frac{2}{3}\pi(729 - 512)$.

5 Volume of cone $= \frac{1}{3}(\pi \times 6^2 \times 18) = 216\pi$ cm³ *[1 mark]*

So $\frac{4}{3}\pi r^3 = 216\pi$ cm³ *[1 mark]*

$r^3 = 162$ *[1 mark]*

$r = 5.4513...$ cm $= 5.45$ cm (3 s.f.) *[1 mark]*

[4 marks available in total — as above]

6 Let r be the radius of the spheres.

Volume of cuboid $= 2r \times 2r \times 4r = 16r^3$ *[1 mark]*

Volume of both spheres $= 2 \times \frac{4}{3}\pi r^3 = \frac{8}{3}\pi r^3$ *[1 mark]*

Percentage of box occupied by spheres $= \dfrac{\frac{8}{3}\pi r^3}{16r^3} \times 100$ *[1 mark]*

$= \frac{800\pi}{48} = 52.4\%$ *[1 mark]*

[4 marks available in total — as above]

7 Cross-sectional area = area of trapezium

$= 0.5 \times (0.7 + 0.4) \times 0.3 = 0.165$ m²

Volume of trough $= 0.165 \times 1.2 = 0.198$ m³ $= 198\,000$ cm³

Rate of flow = 9 litres/minute = 9000 cm³/minute

Time to fill trough $= 198\,000 \div 9000 = 22$ minutes

[4 marks available — 1 mark for calculating volume of trough, 1 mark for converting volume or rate of flow to appropriate units, 1 mark for dividing volume by rate of flow, 1 mark for correct answer]

8 a) Cross-sectional area of pipe: $0.2^2 \times \pi = 0.12566...$ m²

Cross-sectional area of water: $0.12566... \div 2 = 0.06283...$ m² *[1 mark]*

b) Rate of flow = 2520 litres per minute

$= 2520 \div 60$ litres per second

$= 42$ litres per second *[1 mark]*

$= 42\,000$ cm³/s

$= 0.042$ m³/s *[1 mark]*

Speed = Rate of flow ÷ cross-sectional area of water

$= 0.042$ m³/s $\div 0.06283...$ m² *[1 mark]*

$= 0.66845...$ m/s $= 0.668$ m/s (3 s.f.) *[1 mark]*

[4 marks available in total — as above]

Page 80: More Enlargements

1 $1^3 : 7^3 = 1 : 343$ *[1 mark]*

2 Area of enlarged shape $= 7 \times 3^2$ *[1 mark]*

$= 63$ cm² *[1 mark]*

[2 marks available in total — as above]

3 Let x be the scale factor for length from cylinder A to cylinder B.

$x^3 = \frac{64}{27}$, so $x = \sqrt[3]{\frac{64}{27}} = \frac{4}{3}$ *[1 mark]*

Then $x^2 = \frac{4^2}{3^2} = \frac{16}{9}$, so s.a. of cylinder B $= 81\pi \times \frac{16}{9}$ *[1 mark]*

$= 144\pi$ cm² *[1 mark]*

[3 marks available in total — as above]

4 a) Scale factor from **A** to **C**:

$n^2 = 108\pi \div 12\pi = 9$ so $n = 3$

Volume of **A** $= 135\pi$ cm³ $\div 3^3 = 5\pi$ cm³

[4 marks available — 1 mark for finding n², 1 mark for finding n, 1 mark for dividing volume of A by n³, 1 mark for correct answer]

b) Scale factor from **A** to **B**:

$m^2 = 48\pi \div 12\pi = 4$ *[1 mark]*

$m = 2$ *[1 mark]*

Perpendicular height of **B** = 4 cm × 2

$= 8$ cm *[1 mark]*

[3 marks available in total — as above]

Page 81: Projections

1 a)

[1 mark]

b)

[1 mark]

It doesn't matter which way round you've drawn your plan view — just as long as it's the correct shape.

2

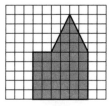

[2 marks available — 1 mark for rectangular part correct, 1 mark for triangular part correct]

Pages 82-83: Loci and Construction

1 a)

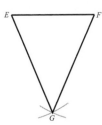

[2 marks available — 1 mark for arcs drawn with a radius of 4.5 cm, 1 mark for completed triangle]

b)

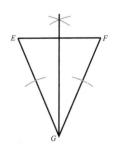

[2 marks available — 1 mark for correct construction arcs, 1 mark for correct bisector]

2 AB = 6 cm, so sides perpendicular to AB have length
$(18 - 6 - 6) \div 2 = 3$ cm

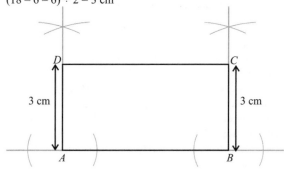

[4 marks available — 1 mark for working out that lines AD and BC are 3 cm, 1 mark for correctly constructing a perpendicular line at A, 1 mark for correctly constructing a perpendicular line at B, 1 mark for a completely correctly constructed rectangle]

The diagram shows just one way of constructing the rectangle.
In the exam, you'll get the marks as long as your construction lines are correct and visible.

3

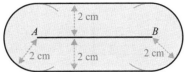

Scale: 1 cm represents 1 m

[2 marks available — 1 mark for correct semicircles, 1 mark for correct shaded area]

4

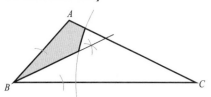

[4 marks available — 1 mark for radius of 6.5 cm with centre at C, 1 mark for construction arcs on AB and BC for angle bisector at ABC, 1 mark for correct angle bisector at ABC, and 1 mark for the correct shading]

Make sure you remember to leave in your construction lines.

5

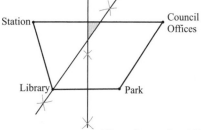

[3 marks available — 1 mark for perpendicular bisector between Library and Park, 1 mark for perpendicular bisector between Station and Park, 1 mark for the correct shaded area]

6

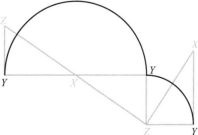

[3 marks available — 1 mark for constructing either the semicircle or quarter circle correctly, 1 mark for the two parts of the locus being joined together, 1 mark for a completely correct diagram]

Page 84: Bearings

1 a)

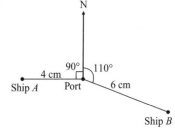

[4 marks available — 1 mark for Ship A 4 cm from the port, 1 mark for correct bearing for ship A, 1 mark for ship B 6 cm from the port, and 1 mark for correct bearing for Ship B]

This diagram has been drawn a bit smaller to make it fit — your measurements should match the labels given on the diagram here.

b) 102° (accept answers between 100° and 104°) *[1 mark]*

c) 180° − 102° = 78°
360° − 78° = 282° (accept answers between 280° and 284°)
[2 marks available — 1 mark for correctly using 102°, 1 mark for correct answer]
You could also do this by adding 180° to 102°.

2 a)

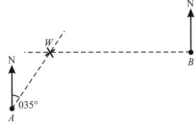

[2 marks available — 1 mark for correct bearing of 035° and 1 mark for marking W directly west of B]

b)

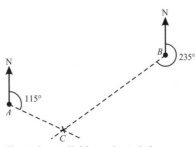

[3 marks available — 1 mark for correct bearing from A, 1 mark for correct bearing from B and 1 mark for correctly identifying intersection at point C]

c) 164° (accept answers between 162° and 166°) *[1 mark]*

Section Six — Pythagoras and Trigonometry

Page 85: Pythagoras' Theorem

1 $AB^2 = 4^2 + 8^2$ *[1 mark]*
   $AB = \sqrt{16 + 64} = \sqrt{80}$ *[1 mark]*
   $AB = 8.94$ cm (2 d.p) *[1 mark]*
   [3 marks available in total — as above]

2 Difference in x-coordinates $= 8 - 2 = 6$
   Difference in y-coordinates $= 8 - -1 = 9$ *[1 mark for both]*
   So length of line segment $= \sqrt{6^2 + 9^2} = \sqrt{36 + 81}$ *[1 mark]*
   $= \sqrt{117} = \sqrt{9 \times 13} = 3\sqrt{13}$ *[1 mark]*
   [3 marks available in total — as above]

3 Let h be the height of the triangle:
   $13^2 = 5^2 + h^2$ *[1 mark]*
   $h = \sqrt{169 - 25} = \sqrt{144}$ *[1 mark]*
   $h = 12$ cm *[1 mark]*
   Area, $A = \frac{1}{2} \times 10 \times 12$
   $A = 60$ cm^2 *[1 mark]*
   [4 marks available in total — as above]

4 Length of EA:
   $28.3^2 = 20^2 + EA^2$ *[1 mark]*
   $EA = \sqrt{800.89 - 400}$
   $EA = 20.02...$ *[1 mark]*
   Length of CE:
   $54.3^2 = 20^2 + CE^2$ *[1 mark]*
   $CE = \sqrt{2948.49 - 400}$
   $CE = 50.48...$ *[1 mark]*
   Perimeter $= 28.3 + 54.3 + EA + CE = 153.1$ cm (1 d.p) *[1 mark]*
   [5 marks available in total — as above]

Page 86: Trigonometry

1 $\sin x = \frac{14}{18}$ *[1 mark]*
   $x = \sin^{-1}\left(\frac{14}{18}\right)$ *[1 mark]*
   $x = 51.1°$ (1 d.p) *[1 mark]*
   [3 marks available in total — as above]

2 $\tan 60° = \frac{4}{y}$ *[1 mark]*
   $y = \frac{4}{\tan 60°}$ *[1 mark]*
   $y = \frac{4}{\sqrt{3}}$ m *[1 mark]*
   [3 marks available in total — as above]

3 Call the distance from the centre of the circle to the centre of an edge x. The radius bisects the interior angle forming angle a.

   Sum of the interior angles of a hexagon $= 4 \times 180° = 720°$
   Each interior angle of a hexagon $= 720° \div 6 = 120°$ *[1 mark]*
   $a = 120 \div 2 = 60°$ *[1 mark]*
   $\sin 60° = \frac{x}{8.5}$ *[1 mark]*
   $x = 8.5 \times \sin 60°$ *[1 mark]*
   $x = 7.36$ cm (2 d.p) *[1 mark]*
   [5 marks available in total — as above]
   You could also use the calculation cos 30° × 8.5 to find the value of x. As long as you make sure you show your working, you'll get full marks if your answer is correct.

4 $\tan 30° + \sin 60° = \frac{1}{\sqrt{3}} + \frac{\sqrt{3}}{2}$ *[1 mark]*
   $= \frac{\sqrt{3}}{3} + \frac{\sqrt{3}}{2} = \frac{2\sqrt{3}}{6} + \frac{3\sqrt{3}}{6}$ *[1 mark]*
   $= \frac{5\sqrt{3}}{6}$ *[1 mark]*
   [3 marks available in total — as above]

Pages 87-88: The Sine and Cosine Rules

1 a) $AC^2 = 10^2 + 7^2 - (2 \times 10 \times 7 \times \cos 85°)$ *[1 mark]*
       $AC = \sqrt{149 - 140 \times \cos 85°}$
       $AC = 11.7$ cm (3 s.f) *[1 mark]*
       [2 marks available in total — as above.]

   b) Area $= \frac{1}{2} \times 10 \times 7 \times \sin 85°$ *[1 mark]*
       Area $= 34.9$ cm^2 (3 s.f) *[1 mark]*
       [2 marks available in total — as above]

2 *First you need to find one angle using the cosine rule.*
   E.g. use angle CAB.
   $\cos A = \frac{14^2 + 12^2 - 19^2}{2 \times 14 \times 12}$ *[1 mark]*
   $A = \cos^{-1}\left(\frac{-21}{336}\right)$
   $A = 93.58...°$ *[1 mark]*
   Area $= \frac{1}{2} \times 14 \times 12 \times \sin 93.58...°$ *[1 mark]*
   Area $= 83.84$ cm^2 (2 d.p) *[1 mark]*
   [4 marks available in total — as above]

3 $\sin 30° = \frac{x}{AC}$
   $AC = \frac{x}{\sin 30°} = 2x$ cm *[1 mark]*
   Angle $CAD = 90° - 30° = 60°$
   $CD^2 = (2x)^2 + (3x)^2 - (2 \times 2x \times 3x \times \cos 60°)$ *[1 mark]*
   $CD^2 = 4x^2 + 9x^2 - 6x^2 = 7x^2$
   $CD = \sqrt{7x^2} = x\sqrt{7}$ cm *[1 mark]*
   Perimeter of $ACD = 2x + 3x + x\sqrt{7}$
   $= (5 + \sqrt{7})x$ cm (so $a = 5$ *[1 mark]*, $b = 7$ *[1 mark]*)
   [5 marks available in total — as above]

4 $\frac{36}{\sin ABC} = \frac{17}{\sin 26°}$ *[1 mark]*
   $\sin ABC = \frac{36 \times \sin 26°}{17}$ *[1 mark]*
   $ABC = 180 - \sin^{-1}\left(\frac{36 \times \sin 26°}{17}\right) = 111.8°$ (1 d.p.) *[1 mark]*
   [3 marks available in total — as above]

5 Angle $ABD = 180° - 90° - 31° - 12° = 47°$
   Angle $ACB = 180° - 12° - 47° = 121°$ *[1 mark for both]*
   Use the sine rule: $\frac{3.3}{\sin 12°} = \frac{AB}{\sin 121°}$
   $AB = \frac{3.3}{\sin 12°} \times \sin 121°$ *[1 mark]*
   $AB = 13.6050...$ m *[1 mark]*

Answers

Find length BD: $\cos 47° = \dfrac{BD}{13.6050...}$

$BD = \cos 47° \times 13.6050...$ *[1 mark]*

$BD = 9.2786... = 9.28$ m (3 s.f.) *[1 mark]*

[5 marks available in total— as above]

There's more than one way of doing this question. As long as you've used a correct method to get the right answer you'll still get the marks.

6   First, split $ABCD$ into two triangles, ABC and ACD.

$\dfrac{55}{\sin ACB} = \dfrac{93}{\sin 116°}$ *[1 mark]*

$\sin ACB = \dfrac{\sin 116°}{93} \times 55$

Angle $ACB = \sin^{-1}(0.531...) = 32.109...°$ *[1 mark]*

Angle $BAC = 180° - 116° - 32.109...°$ so,

Area of $ABC = \dfrac{1}{2} \times 93 \times 55 \times \sin(180 - 116 - 32.10...)°$ *[1 mark]*

$= 1351.106...$ cm^2 *[1 mark]*

Angle $ACD = 78° - 32.109...°$ so

Area of $ACD = \dfrac{1}{2} \times 93 \times 84 \times \sin(78 - 32.10...)°$

$= 2804.531...$ cm^2 *[1 mark]*

Area of $ABCD = 1351.106... + 2804.531... = 4155.637...$

$= 4160$ cm^2 (3 s.f.) *[1 mark]*

[6 marks available in total — as above]

Page 89: 3D Pythagoras and Trigonometry

1   $BH^2 = 6^2 + 3^2 + 4^2$ *[1 mark]*

$BH = \sqrt{61}$ *[1 mark]*

$BH = 7.81$ cm (3 s.f) *[1 mark]*

[3 marks available in total — as above]

2   $FG = 80 \div 2 \div 8 = 5$ cm

$DF^2 = 8^2 + 2^2 + 5^2$ *[1 mark]*

$DF = \sqrt{93}$ *[1 mark]*

You could also calculate the length of either AG, BH, or CE.

The angle between the stick and the place $CDHG$ is the angle between the line DF and the line DG, so

$\sin FDG = \dfrac{5}{\sqrt{93}}$ *[1 mark]*

$FDG = \sin^{-1}\left(\dfrac{5}{\sqrt{93}}\right)$ *[1 mark]* $= 31°$ (2 s.f.) *[1 mark]*

[5 marks available in total — as above]

Pages 90-91: Vectors

1   a) $\begin{pmatrix} -3 \\ 5 \end{pmatrix} - \begin{pmatrix} 5 \\ 4 \end{pmatrix} = \begin{pmatrix} -8 \\ 1 \end{pmatrix}$ *[1 mark]*

b) $4 \times \begin{pmatrix} 5 \\ 4 \end{pmatrix} - \begin{pmatrix} -4 \\ -6 \end{pmatrix} = \begin{pmatrix} 20 \\ 16 \end{pmatrix} - \begin{pmatrix} -4 \\ -6 \end{pmatrix} = \begin{pmatrix} 24 \\ 22 \end{pmatrix}$ *[1 mark]*

c) $2 \times \begin{pmatrix} -3 \\ 5 \end{pmatrix} + \begin{pmatrix} 5 \\ 4 \end{pmatrix} + 3 \times \begin{pmatrix} -4 \\ -6 \end{pmatrix} = \begin{pmatrix} -6 \\ 10 \end{pmatrix} + \begin{pmatrix} 5 \\ 4 \end{pmatrix} + \begin{pmatrix} -12 \\ -18 \end{pmatrix}$

$= \begin{pmatrix} -13 \\ -4 \end{pmatrix}$ *[1 mark]*

2   a) $4\mathbf{a} + 3\mathbf{b}$ *[1 mark]*

b) $4\mathbf{a} + 1.5\mathbf{b}$ *[1 mark]*

3   a) $\overrightarrow{CD} = -2\mathbf{a}$ *[1 mark]*

b) $\overrightarrow{AC} = 2\mathbf{d} + 2\mathbf{a}$ *[1 mark]*

c) $\overrightarrow{BL} = \mathbf{d} - \mathbf{a}$ *[1 mark]*

4   a) $\overrightarrow{OM} = \overrightarrow{OA} + \overrightarrow{AM} = \overrightarrow{OA} + \dfrac{1}{2}\overrightarrow{AB}$ *[1 mark]*

$\overrightarrow{AB} = \mathbf{b} - 2\mathbf{a}$ or $-2\mathbf{a} + \mathbf{b}$

$\overrightarrow{OM} = 2\mathbf{a} + \dfrac{1}{2}(-2\mathbf{a} + \mathbf{b})$ or $\overrightarrow{OM} = 2\mathbf{a} + \dfrac{1}{2}(\mathbf{b} - 2\mathbf{a})$

$= \mathbf{a} + \dfrac{1}{2}\mathbf{b}$ *[1 mark]*

[2 marks available in total — as above]

b) $\overrightarrow{OX} = \overrightarrow{OA} + \overrightarrow{AX}$ *[1 mark]*

As AX:XB = 1:3, AX must be one quarter of AB, so:

$\overrightarrow{OX} = \overrightarrow{OA} + \dfrac{1}{4}\overrightarrow{AB}$

$\overrightarrow{OX} = 2\mathbf{a} + \dfrac{1}{4}(\mathbf{b} - 2\mathbf{a})$ *[1 mark]*

$\overrightarrow{OX} = \dfrac{3}{2}\mathbf{a} + \dfrac{1}{4}\mathbf{b}$ *[1 mark]*

[3 marks available in total — as above]

5   a) $\overrightarrow{BX} = \overrightarrow{BC} + \overrightarrow{CX}$

$\overrightarrow{BC} = 6\overrightarrow{BW} = 6\mathbf{b}$ *[1 mark]*

As AX = 2XC, CX must be one third of CA, so:

$\overrightarrow{CX} = \dfrac{1}{3}\overrightarrow{CA}$ *[1 mark]*

$\overrightarrow{CA} = -3\mathbf{a} - 6\mathbf{b}$ *[1 mark]*

$\overrightarrow{CX} = \dfrac{1}{3}(-3\mathbf{a} - 6\mathbf{b}) = -\mathbf{a} - 2\mathbf{b}$

$\overrightarrow{BX} = 6\mathbf{b} - \mathbf{a} - 2\mathbf{b} = 4\mathbf{b} - \mathbf{a}$ *[1 mark]*

[4 marks available in total — as above]

There are other ways of doing this one — you could start by writing $\overrightarrow{BX}$ as $\overrightarrow{BA} + \overrightarrow{AX}$ instead.

b) From part a) $\overrightarrow{BX} = 4\mathbf{b} - \mathbf{a}$:

$ABCD$ is a parallelogram, so:

$\overrightarrow{CD} = \overrightarrow{BA} = -\overrightarrow{AB} = -3\mathbf{a}$ *[1 mark]*

$\overrightarrow{CM} = \dfrac{1}{2}\overrightarrow{CD} = -\dfrac{3}{2}\mathbf{a}$ *[1 mark]*

$\overrightarrow{BM} = \overrightarrow{BC} + \overrightarrow{CM}$

$= 6\mathbf{b} - \dfrac{3}{2}\mathbf{a} = \dfrac{3}{2}(4\mathbf{b} - \mathbf{a})$ *[1 mark]*

B, X and M must be three points on a straight line because the lines BM and BX are both scalar multiples of the vector $4\mathbf{b} - \mathbf{a}$. *[1 mark]*

[4 marks available in total — as above]

There are other ways of doing this bit too — for example, you could show that XM and BX are scalar multiples of each other.

Section Seven — Probability and Statistics

Page 92: Probability Basics

1   a) P(strawberry) $= \dfrac{2}{2 + 5} = \dfrac{2}{7}$ *[1 mark]*

b) P(banana) $= \dfrac{5}{7}$

$2 \times$ P(strawberry) $= 2 \times \dfrac{2}{7} = \dfrac{4}{7}$ so Amy is wrong,

she is more than twice as likely to pick a banana sweet.

[2 marks available — 1 mark for finding the probability of choosing a banana sweet, 1 mark for saying Amy is wrong with a valid explanation]

2   Number of red counters $= p - n$ *[1 mark]*

Probability of getting a red counter $= \dfrac{p - n}{p}$ *[1 mark]*

[2 marks available in total — as above]

3   P(stripy sock) $= 2y$ *[1 mark]*

$0.4 + y + 2y = 1$ *[1 mark]*

$3y = 0.6$

$y = 0.2$ *[1 mark]*

[3 marks available in total — as above]

Page 93: Counting Outcomes

1

		Dice					
		1	2	3	4	5	6
Cards	2	3	4	5	6	7	8
	4	5	6	7	8	9	10
	6	7	8	9	10	11	12
	8	9	10	11	12	13	14
	10	11	12	13	14	15	16

P(scoring more than 4) $= \dfrac{\text{number of ways to score more than 4}}{\text{total number of possible outcomes}}$

$= \dfrac{28}{30} = \dfrac{14}{15}$

[3 marks available — 1 mark for finding the total number of possible outcomes, 1 mark for finding the number of ways to score more than 4, 1 mark for the correct answer]

2 Combinations of sandwich and drink = 5 × 8 = 40
   Combinations of sandwich and snack = 5 × 4 = 20
   Combinations of sandwich, snack and drink = 5 × 4 × 8 = 160
   Total number of possible combinations = 40 + 20 + 160 = 220
   *[3 marks available — 1 mark for the correct number of
   combinations for one meal deal, 1 mark for the correct number
   of combinations for the other two meal deals, 1 mark for the
   correct answer]*

3 a) Total number of different ways for the spinners to land
      = 4 × 4 × 4 × 4 × 4 = 4^5 = 1024 *[1 mark]*
   b) Number of ways of not spinning any 1's = 3 × 3 × 3 × 3 × 3
      = 3^5 = 243 *[1 mark]*
      So P(not spinning any 1's) = $\frac{243}{1024}$ *[1 mark]*
      [2 marks available in total — as above]

4 a) 4 × 4 × 4 × 4 × 4 × 4 = 4096 *[1 mark]*
   b) Number of ways for all lights to be red or blue
      = 2 × 2 × 2 × 2 × 2 × 2 = 64 *[1 mark]*
      P(all lights red or blue) = $\frac{64}{4096} = \frac{1}{64}$ *[1 mark]*
      [2 marks available in total — as above]

Pages 94-95: Probability Experiments

1 a) 50 × 0.12 = 6
      *[2 marks available — 1 mark for correct method,
      1 mark for the correct answer]*
   b) E.g. On a fair dice, the theoretical frequency of each number is
      0.166..., so as 1 has a much higher relative frequency and 5 has
      a much lower relative frequency, the dice is probably not fair.
      *[2 marks available —1 mark for 'not fair' or similar, 1 mark
      for an explanation including numbers or relative frequency]*
   c) E.g. no, each dice roll is random, so in a small number of
      trials like 50 she is likely to get different results.
      [1 mark]

2 a)

Number on counter	1	2	3	4	5
Frequency	23	25	22	21	9
Relative Frequency	0.23	0.25	0.22	0.21	0.09

   *[2 marks available — 2 marks for all correct answers,
   otherwise 1 mark for any frequency ÷ 100]*
   b) Elvin is likely to be wrong. The bag seems to contain fewer
      counters numbered 5. *[1 mark]*
   c) P(odd number) = 0.23 + 0.22 + 0.09 *[1 mark]*
      = 0.54 *[1 mark]*
      [2 marks available in total — as above]

3 a) i) $\frac{1}{2}$ × 8 = 4 *[1 mark]*
      ii) E.g. Danielle predicted correctly five times, which is close
          to the number you'd expect her to get correct if she was just
          guessing, so there is no evidence that she can predict the flip
          of a coin. *[1 mark]*
   b) i)

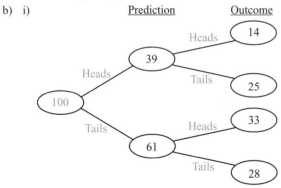

   *[3 marks available — 1 mark for the numbers 39 and 61
   in the correct places, 1 mark for the numbers 14 and 25 in
   the correct places, 1 mark for the numbers 33 and 28 in
   the correct places]*

   ii) Relative frequency of predicting the outcome correctly
       = relative frequency of heads, heads or tails, tails.
       = $\frac{14 + 28}{100} = \frac{42}{100}$ or $\frac{21}{50}$ or 0.42
       *[2 marks available — 1 mark for 14 + 28,
       1 mark for the correct answer]*
   c) E.g. The experiment in part b) has more trials so the results are
      more reliable. *[1 mark]*

Page 96: The AND / OR Rules

1 a) P(prime number) = 0.15 + 0.2 + 0.1 = 0.45
      P(multiple of 2) = 0.15 + 0.25 = 0.4
      P(a prime multiple of 2) = 0.15
      P(prime number or multiple of 2) = 0.45 + 0.4 – 0.15 = 0.7
      *[2 marks available — 1 mark for a correct method,
      1 mark for the correct answer]*
      *Alternatively you work out which numbers are prime or multiples
      of two: 2, 3, 4 and 5. Then add the probabilities of these outcomes
      together 0.15 + 0.2 + 0.25 + 0.1 = 0.7.*
   b) i) P(spun twice) = P(1st spin isn't 2) × P(2nd spin is 2)
          = (1 – 0.15) × 0.15 *[1 mark]*
          = 0.85 × 0.15 = 0.1275 *[1 mark]*
          [2 marks available — as above]
      ii) P(spun more than twice) = 1 – P(spun twice or once)
          = 1 – (0.1275 + 0.15) *[1 mark]*
          = 1 – 0.2775 = 0.7225 *[1 mark]*
          [2 marks available — as above]

2 a) P(losing) = 1 – 0.3 = 0.7
      P(losing 3 games) = 0.7 × 0.7 × 0.7 = 0.343 *[1 mark]*
   b) P(wins at least 1 prize) = 1 – P(doesn't win a prize)
      = 1 – (0.7 × 0.7) *[1 mark]*
      = 1 – 0.49 = 0.51 *[1 mark]*
      [2 marks available in total — as above]
   c) P(winning 1 prize in 3 games)
      = P(win, lose, lose) + P(lose, win, lose) + P(lose, lose, win)
      = (0.3 × 0.7 × 0.7) + (0.7 × 0.3 × 0.7) + (0.7 × 0.7 × 0.3)
      [1 mark]
      = 0.147 + 0.147 + 0.147 = 0.441 *[1 mark]*
      Shaun is wrong, there is only a 44.1% chance of winning
      exactly once in 3 games. *[1 mark]*
      [3 marks available in total — as above]

Pages 97: Tree Diagrams

1 a)
      Jo   Heather
                              $\frac{1}{4}$ Burgundy
                                                  trousers
              $\frac{2}{5}$ Burgundy
                              trousers
                                          $\frac{3}{4}$ Not
                                                          burgundy
                                                          trousers
              $\frac{3}{5}$ $\frac{1}{4}$ Burgundy
                              Not   trousers
                              burgundy
      [1 mark]   trousers
                                          $\frac{3}{4}$ Not
                                                          burgundy
                                                          trousers
                              [1 mark]
      [2 marks available in total — as above]
   b) P(neither wear burgundy trousers) = $\frac{3}{5} \times \frac{3}{4}$ *[1 mark]*
      = $\frac{9}{20}$ *[1 mark]*
      [2 marks available in total — as above]

Answers

2 a) P(Paul's point) = P(1, 2, 3 or 6) = $\frac{2}{3}$

P(Jen's point) = $1 - \frac{2}{3} = \frac{1}{3}$ *[1 mark for both probabilities]*

You can draw a tree diagram to help you:

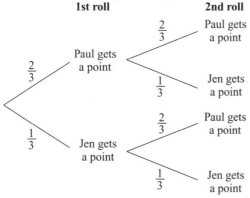

1st roll   **2nd roll**

P(they draw after two rolls) = P(they both get 1 point)

= $\left(\frac{2}{3} \times \frac{1}{3}\right) + \left(\frac{1}{3} \times \frac{2}{3}\right)$ *[1 mark]*

= $\frac{2}{9} + \frac{2}{9} = \frac{4}{9}$ *[1 mark]*

[3 marks available in total — as above]

b) P(Paul wins) = P(Paul wins 3-0) + P(Paul wins 2-1)

= $\left(\frac{2}{3} \times \frac{2}{3} \times \frac{2}{3}\right) + \left(\frac{2}{3} \times \frac{2}{3} \times \frac{1}{3}\right) + \left(\frac{2}{3} \times \frac{1}{3} \times \frac{2}{3}\right) + \left(\frac{1}{3} \times \frac{2}{3} \times \frac{2}{3}\right)$

= $\frac{8}{27} + \frac{4}{27} + \frac{4}{27} + \frac{4}{27} = \frac{20}{27}$

[3 marks available — 1 mark for finding the probability of Paul winning 3-0, 1 mark for finding the probabilities of Paul winning 2-1, 1 mark for the correct final answer]

You could draw another tree diagram showing 3 rolls if you're struggling to find the right probabilities.

Page 98: Conditional Probability

1 a)

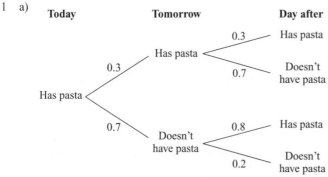

Today   **Tomorrow**   **Day after**

[2 marks available — 1 mark for the correct probabilities for tomorrow, 1 mark for the correct probabilities for the day after]

b) P(pasta on 1 of the next 2 days) = P(pasta then no pasta)
                 + P(no pasta then pasta)

= $(0.3 \times 0.7) + (0.7 \times 0.8)$ *[1 mark]*

= $0.21 + 0.56 = 0.77$ *[1 mark]*

[2 marks available in total — as above]

2 a) P(2nd milk given 1st is milk) = $\frac{6}{11}$ *[1 mark]*

1 milk chocolate has been taken, so there are 6 milk chocolates left out of 11 remaining chocolates.

b) P(at least one milk) = 1 − P(no milk)

                 = 1 − P(white then white)

                 = $1 - \left(\frac{5}{12} \times \frac{4}{11}\right)$ *[1 mark]*

                 = $1 - \frac{20}{132} = \frac{112}{132} = \frac{28}{33}$ *[1 mark]*

[2 marks available in total — as above]

c) P(milk and white) = P(milk then white) + P(white then milk)

= $\left(\frac{7}{12} \times \frac{5}{11}\right) + \left(\frac{5}{12} \times \frac{7}{11}\right)$ *[1 mark]*

= $\frac{35}{66}$ *[1 mark]*

[2 marks available in total — as above]

You might find it helpful to draw a tree diagram for parts b) and c).

Page 99-100: Sets and Venn Diagrams

1 a) $(x + 4) + 3x + (2x + 3) + 9 = 40$

$6x + 16 = 40$ *[1 mark]*

$6x = 24$

$x = 4$ *[1 mark]*

[2 marks available in total — as above]

b) n($A \cap B$) = $3x = 12$ *[1 mark]*

P($A \cap B$) = $\frac{12}{40} = \frac{3}{10}$ *[1 mark]*

[2 marks available in total — as above]

2 a) P(neither) = 1 − P(pie or drink)

               = 1 − (P(pie) + P(drink) − P(both)) *[1 mark]*

               = 1 − (0.33 + 0.64 − 0.27) = 0.3 *[1 mark]*

[2 marks available in total — as above]

You could also find the probabilities of only getting a pie and only getting a drink (see below) and then work out 1 − (P(only a pie) + P(only a drink) + P(both)).

b) P(only a pie) = 0.33 − 0.27 = 0.06   P(both) = 0.27

P(only a drink) = 0.64 − 0.27 = 0.37   P(neither) = 0.3

Multiply each probability by 4000 to find expected frequencies:

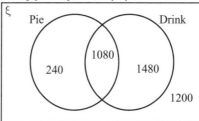

[3 marks available — 1 mark for P(only a pie) and P(only a drink), 1 mark for multiplying each probability by 4000, 1 mark for a completely correct Venn diagram]

c) P(pie given no drink) = $\frac{240}{1440} = \frac{1}{6}$

[2 marks available — 1 mark for finding the expected number of people who don't get a drink (correct denominator), 1 mark for the correct answer]

3 P(male given singer) = $\frac{21}{54} = \frac{7}{18}$

[2 marks available — 1 mark for finding the percentage of singers (correct denominator), 1 mark for the correct answer]

4 a)

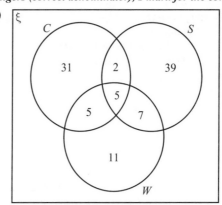

[3 marks available — 3 marks for a completely correct diagram, otherwise 1 mark for at least 2 correct entries or 2 marks for at least 4 correct entries]

b) $\frac{31 + 5 + 5 + 2 + 7 + 39}{100} = \frac{89}{100}$ or 0.89 *[1 mark]*

c) $\frac{7 + 5}{11 + 5 + 5 + 7}$ *[1 mark]*

= $\frac{12}{28} = \frac{3}{7}$ *[1 mark]*

[2 marks available in total — as above]

Page 101: Sampling and Data Collection

1 a) E.g.

Number of chocolate bars	Tally	Frequency
0-2		
3-5		
6-8		
9-11		
12 or more		

[2 marks available — 1 mark for a suitable tally table, 1 mark for non-overlapping classes that cover all possible values]

b) E.g. Faye's results are likely to be biased because she hasn't selected her sample at random from all the teenagers in the UK. Also, her sample is too small to represent the whole population. So Faye can't use her results to draw conclusions about teenagers in the UK.
[2 marks available — 1 mark for a correct comment based on bias or sample size, 1 mark for stating that Faye can't draw conclusions about teenagers in the UK with reasoning]

2 a) Proportion of people in sample who travelled by car
= 22 ÷ 50 = 0.44 *[1 mark]*
Estimate of number of people at match who travelled by car
= 0.44 × 5000 *[1 mark]* = 2200 *[1 mark]*
[3 marks available in total — as above]

b) E.g. Daisy has made the assumption that Mario's sample is a fair representation of the people at her match. *[1 mark]*
Or you could say she has assumed that the proportions who travelled by car to the two matches are roughly the same.
E.g. her estimate is unreliable because she hasn't sampled people from the correct population. *[1 mark]*
[2 marks available in total — as above]

Page 102: Mean, Median, Mode and Range

1 a) Yes, the mean number is higher than 17 because the 11th data value is higher than the mean of the original 10 values.
[1 mark]

b) You can't tell if the median number is higher than 15, because you don't know the other data values.
[1 mark]

2 a) 23, 26, 36 (in any order)
range = 13, median = 26
[2 marks available — 1 mark for all three weights correct, 1 mark for both range and median correct]

b) 32 + 23 + 31 + 28 + 36 + 26 = 176
4 × 27.25 = 109 *[1 mark]*
176 − 109 = 67 *[1 mark]*
so, goats weighing 31 kg and 36 kg *[1 mark]*
[3 marks available in total — as above]

3 Call the five consecutive numbers n, $n + 1$, $n + 2$, $n + 3$ and $n + 4$
Median = middle value = $n + 2$
Mean = $\dfrac{n + (n + 1) + (n + 2) + (n + 3) + (n + 4)}{5}$
$= \dfrac{5n + 10}{5}$
$= n + 2$
Difference between mean and median = $(n + 2) - (n + 2) = 0$
[3 marks available — 1 mark for writing correct expressions for five consecutive numbers, 1 mark for a correct expression for the mean, 1 mark for showing that the difference between the expression for the mean and the expression for the median is zero]

Page 103: Grouped Frequency Tables

1 a) The modal class is the one with the highest frequency, so that's $3 \leq x \leq 5$ *[1 mark]*

b) $(10 + 1) ÷ 2 = 5.5$, so the median is halfway between the 5th and 6th values, so it lies in the group containing the 5th and 6th values, which is $3 \leq x \leq 5$ *[1 mark]*

c) $(1 \times 2) + (4 \times 4) + (7 \times 3) + (10 \times 1) ÷ 10$
$= 49 ÷ 10 = 4.9$ cm
[4 marks available — 1 mark for all mid-interval values, 1 mark for calculation of frequency × mid-interval value, 1 mark for dividing sum of frequency × mid-interval values by sum of frequencies, 1 mark for the correct answer]

2 a) $(24 \times 4) + (28 \times 8) + (32 \times 13) + (36 \times 6) + (40 \times 1) ÷ 32$
$= 992 ÷ 32 = 31$ seconds
[4 marks available — 1 mark for all mid-interval values, 1 mark for calculation of frequency × mid-interval value, 1 mark for dividing sum of frequency × mid-interval values by sum of frequencies, 1 mark for the correct answer]

b) There were 32 pupils and $13 + 6 + 1 = 20$ got a time of more than 30 seconds *[1 mark]*, $(20 ÷ 32) \times 100 = 62.5\%$ *[1 mark]*
[2 marks available in total — as above]

c) E.g. You couldn't use these results because you don't know the ages of the pupils in the sample, or whether any of the times were run by boys, so you can't tell if the results would fairly represent 16-year-old boys. *[1 mark for a sensible comment]*

Page 104: Box Plots

1 a) IQR = 72 − 52 *[1 mark]*
= 20 km *[1 mark]*
[2 marks available in total — as above]

b) The interquartile range doesn't include outliers, so it should be a more reliable measure of the spread. *[1 mark]*

c) Harry:

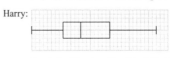

0   20   40   60   80   100 120 140
Distance cycled (km)

[2 marks available — 2 marks for a fully correct box plot, otherwise 1 mark for correctly showing at least 3 of lower endpoint, upper endpoint, median, lower quartile and upper quartile]

d) E.g. comparing the box plots, the IQR of Rachel's distances is much smaller than the IQR of Harry's distances and Rachel's range is also smaller, so I agree that her distances were more consistent.
[2 marks available — 1 mark for correctly comparing the values of the range or IQR, 1 mark for a correct conclusion (supported by a correct comparison)]

2 E.g. the median time taken by the boys is the same as the median time taken by the girls, so on average the boys and girls took the same time. The interquartile range for the boys is smaller than the interquartile range for the girls, so the times taken by the boys were more consistent than the times taken by the girls.
[2 marks available — 1 mark for a correct comparison of the median, 1 mark for a correct comparison of the interquartile range OR range (for both marks, at least one comparison must be given in the context of the data)]
'In the context of the data' means you need to explain what your comparison shows about the times taken by the boys and girls.

Answers

Pages 105-106: Cumulative Frequency

1 a)

Exam mark (%)	≤ 20	≤ 30	≤ 40	≤ 50	≤ 60	≤ 70	≤ 80	≤ 100
Cumulative Frequency	3	13	25	49	91	107	116	120

[1 mark]

b)

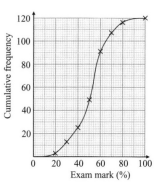

[3 marks available — 1 mark for all points plotted at correct class boundaries, 1 mark for all points plotted at correct heights, 1 mark for joining them with a smooth curve or straight lines]

A common mistake in exams is not plotting the points at the top end of the interval. But you wouldn't make that mistake, would you?

c) Median plotted at 60 gives a value of 53%
[1 mark, accept answers ± 1%]

d) Lower quartile at 30 gives a value of 43%
Upper quartile at 90 gives a value of 60%
Inter-quartile range = 60 − 43 = 17%
[2 marks available — 1 mark for correct method, 1 mark for correct answer, accept answers ± 2%]

e) $\frac{1}{5}$ of pupils got lower than grade 5,

$\frac{1}{5}$ of 120 = 24 pupils

Reading from the graph at a cumulative frequency of 24 gives 39% , so the mark needed to get a grade 5 was about 39%.
[3 marks available — 1 mark for finding the number of pupils who got lower than grade 5, 1 mark for drawing a line across from 24 on the cumulative frequency axis, 1 mark for an answer in the range 37-41%]

2 a) i) Number of journeys between 27 and 47 mins = 49 − 28 = 21
[2 marks available — 1 mark for reading the cumulative frequencies off at 27 and 47 minutes, 1 mark for correct answer]

ii) 48 journeys took 40 minutes or less, so 2 journeys took longer. Percentage of total number = (2 ÷ 50) × 100 = 4%
[2 marks available — 1 mark for correct method, 1 mark for correct answer]

b) The answers are estimates because they're based on grouped data, rather than the actual data values. *[1 mark]*

c)

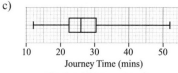

[3 marks available — 1 mark for plotting end points correctly, 1 mark for plotting median correctly (± 0.5) and 1 mark for plotting lower and upper quartiles correctly (± 0.5)]

Pages 107-108: Histograms and Frequency Density

1 To find the scale, find the frequency density of one bar.
Frequency density = frequency ÷ class width = 15 ÷ 20 = 0.75.
So the height of the first bar is 0.75.

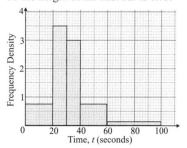

Time, t (s)	Frequency
$0 < t \le 20$	15
$20 < t \le 30$	35
$30 < t \le 40$	30
$40 < t \le 60$	15
$60 < t \le 100$	5

[3 marks available — 1 mark for the correct scale on the frequency density axis, 1 mark for the correct entry in the table, 1 mark for the correct bar on the histogram]

2 *This question is asking you to estimate the mean amount of time the children watched TV for, then compare that to the mean time for the adults.*

Time, m (minutes)	Frequency (f)	Mid-interval Value (x)	fx
$40 \le m < 60$	20 × 1 = 20	50	1000
$60 \le m < 70$	10 × 7 = 70	65	4550
$70 \le m < 80$	10 × 4 = 40	75	3000
$80 \le m < 120$	40 × 2 = 80	100	8000
$120 \le m < 140$	20 × 3 = 60	130	7800
Total	270		24 350

Mean for children = 24 350 ÷ 270 = 90.185...
= 90.2 minutes (to 1 d.p.)

E.g. the data supports the hypothesis since the mean time for the adults is longer than the mean time for the children, and the large samples mean the results should represent the population.
[4 marks available — 1 mark for a correct method to find the frequencies, 1 mark for multiplying the frequencies by the mid-interval values, 1 mark for the correct mean, 1 mark for a correct conclusion based on a comparison of the means]

3 a) Estimate of number of lambs between 3.5 and 4 kg
= 0.5 × 22 *[1 mark]* = 11
11 + (1 × 26) + (1 × 16) + (2 × 3) *[1 mark]*
= 59 out of 100 = 59% *[1 mark]*
[3 marks available in total — as above]

b)

Weight, w kg	$0 < w \leq 2$	$2 < w \leq 4$	$4 < w \leq 5$	$5 < w \leq 6$	$6 < w \leq 8$
Frequency	4	28	30	28	10
Frequency Density	2	14	30	28	5

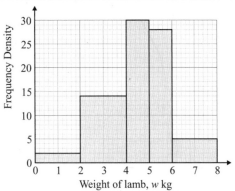

[3 marks available — 1 mark for the correct frequency densities, 1 mark for correctly labelling the axes and drawing 5 bars with no gaps, 1 mark for the correct histogram]

c) E.g. the second histogram shows more lambs with heavier weights and fewer with lighter weights than the first, which suggests there is a difference between the two farms.
[1 mark for a correct comment based on a comparison of the histograms]

Pages 109-110: Time Series and Scatter Graphs

1 a) E.g. there is a pattern in the data that repeats itself every four points. *[1 mark]*

b) $(0 + 56 + 34 + 6) \div 4 = 24$

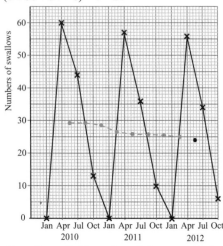

[2 marks available — 1 mark for correct calculation of moving average, 1 mark for plotting the value correctly on the graph]

c) The data shows a downward trend in the numbers of swallows seen. *[1 mark]*

2 a)

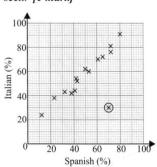

[1 mark]

b) Strong positive correlation *[1 mark]*

c)

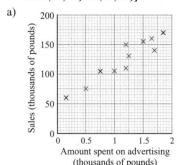

[1 mark for line of best fit passing between (10, 16) & (10, 28) and (80, 82) & (80, 96)]

3 a)

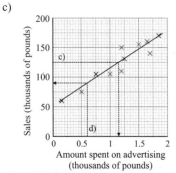

[1 mark if all three points are plotted correctly]

b) As the amount spent on advertising increases, so does the value of sales. *[1 mark]*
Or you could say there's a positive correlation between the amount spent and the value of sales.

c)

See graph — £1150
[2 marks available — 1 mark for drawing a line of best fit, 1 mark for reading off the correct answer, allow answers ± £100]

d) See graph above — £90 000
[1 mark, allow answers ± £10 000]

e) E.g. using the trend to predict sales for values over £3000 might be unreliable because those values are outside their range of data and they don't know whether the same pattern would continue. However, the data shows strong positive correlation, so the trend will probably continue.
[2 marks available — 1 mark for each sensible comment]

Answers